Key Stage 2
Numeracy Practice Book Year 5

Authors

Peter Patilla & Paul Broadbent

Letts
EDUCATIONAL

Every effort has been made to trace copyright holders and to obtain their permission for the use of copyright material. The authors and publishers will gladly receive information enabling them to rectify any error or omission in subsequent editions.

First published 1998
Reprinted 1998 (twice)
Reprinted 1999, 2001
This edition 2000

Letts Educational Limited
The Chiswick Centre,
414 Chiswick High Road,
Chiswick,
London W4 5TF
Tel: 020 8996 3333
Fax: 020 8742 8390

Text © Peter Patilla and Paul Broadbent

Design, page layout and production: Moondisks Ltd, Cambridge
Illustrations: Jeffrey Reid, Moondisks
Cover: Ken Vail Graphics

British Library Cataloguing-in-Publication Data
A CIP record for this book is available from the British Library

ISBN 1 84085 059 0

Printed in Italy

Letts Educational Limited, a division of Granada Learning Limited.
Part of the Granada Media Group.

Introduction
to Year 5 Numeracy Practice Book

Numeracy Skills Year 5

This book has been written to develop and improve the numeracy skills of all pupils in Year 5 (ages 9–10).

Each of the eleven units of work begins with a double page spread of helpful information. This includes:

- ✓ knowledge needed
- ✓ helpful teaching notes
- ✓ table of what should be learned during the course of the unit

Some pages of activities begin with a Key Skill necessary to successfully complete the activities which follow. Pupils should complete and mark these using the Key Skills answers at the back of the book.

At the end of each unit of work is a summary. This can act both as a quick assessment or as a way to decide which parts of the unit a pupil may omit, or may need to practise further.

Contents

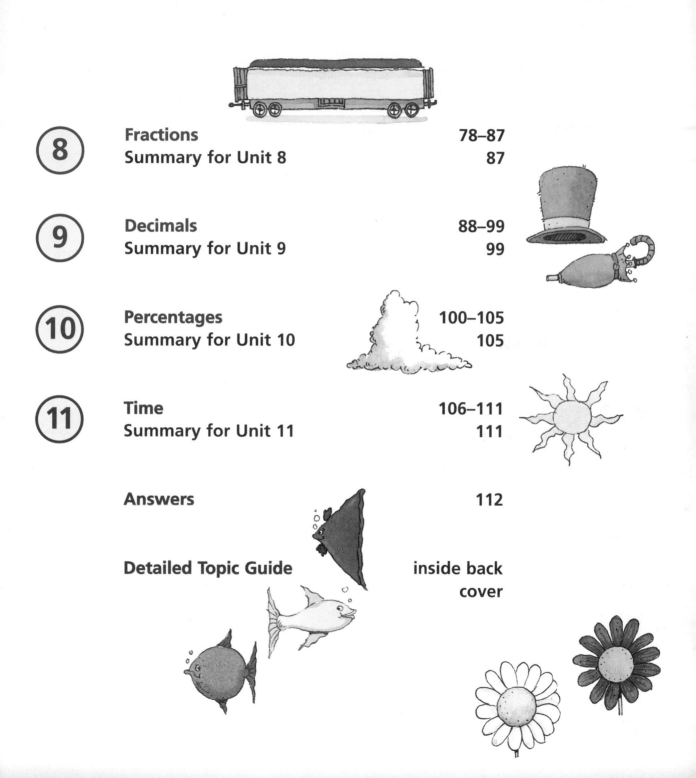

Knowledge needed
✓ recall of addition and subtraction facts to 20
✓ language of addition and subtraction facts
✓ multiplication and division facts for 2, 5 and 10

Helpful facts

Anyway round
The order of adding or multiplying two numbers does not matter:
$7 + 8 = 8 + 7$ $4 \times 6 = 6 \times 4$

Pairs which total 10
The number pairs which total 10 are very important:
10,0   9,1   8,2   7,3   6,4   5,5

Quick methods
Add on 9:
+ 10 then −1 $26 + 9 = 35$
Subtract 9:
− 10 then add 1 $45 - 9 = 36$

Difference
To find the number difference between two numbers, subtract them:
8   13
The difference between them is 5:
$13 - 8 = 5$

Brackets
When brackets are used, work out the sum in brackets first:
$17 - (4 \times 3)$

work out first, then
$17 - 12 = 5$

Using known facts
Use the facts for the 2x, 5x and 10x tables to help work out others:
$5 \times 7 = 35$ So 6×7 is 7 more ... 42

Odd and even numbers

Adding two odd numbers always makes an even number: $3 + 5 = 8$

Subtracting two odd numbers always makes an even number: $9 - 3 = 6$

Adding odd and even numbers always makes an odd number: $3 + 8 = 11$

Subtracting odd and even numbers always makes an odd number: $12 - 3 = 9$ $15 - 4 = 11$

Doubling and halving

Multiplying by 5, multiply by 10 then halve: $7 \times 5 = \frac{1}{2}$ of $70 = 35$

Multiplying by 4, double then double again: 9×4 Double $9 = 18$ Double $18 = 36$

Multiplying by 8, double, double then double again: 8×3 $3 \times 2 \times 2 \times 2 = 24$

Multiplying by 6, multiply by 3 then double: 7×6 $7 \times 3 = 21 \times 2 = 42$

Inverse operations

Division is the opposite of multiplication:
$9 \times 6 = 54$ $54 \div 6 = 9$

Learning outcomes for UNIT 1

✓ knows addition and subtraction bonds to 20
✓ knows addition and subtraction are inverses
✓ can find differences
✓ uses mental strategies to work out number facts from known number facts
✓ knows addition is commutative, e.g. $7 + 6 = 6 + 7$
✓ uses brackets in simple calculations
✓ knows and uses language of addition and subtraction
✓ knows 2x, 5x, 10x tables by heart, and the related division facts
✓ knows 3x, 4x tables by heart, and the related division facts
✓ knows 6x, 7x, 8x, 9x tables by heart, and the related division facts
✓ knows multiplication is commutative, e.g. $8 \times 6 = 6 \times 8$
✓ knows multiplication and division are inverses
✓ knows when to round up and when to round down with remainders

Addition Facts

A

Write the answers.

1. 7 + 4   4. 7 + 7   7. 7 + 5   10. 4 + 5

2. 3 + 6   5. 8 + 3   8. 9 + 6   11. 9 + 2

3. 5 + 9   6. 8 + 9   9. 8 + 4   12. 6 + 6

B

Write the totals of the number groups.

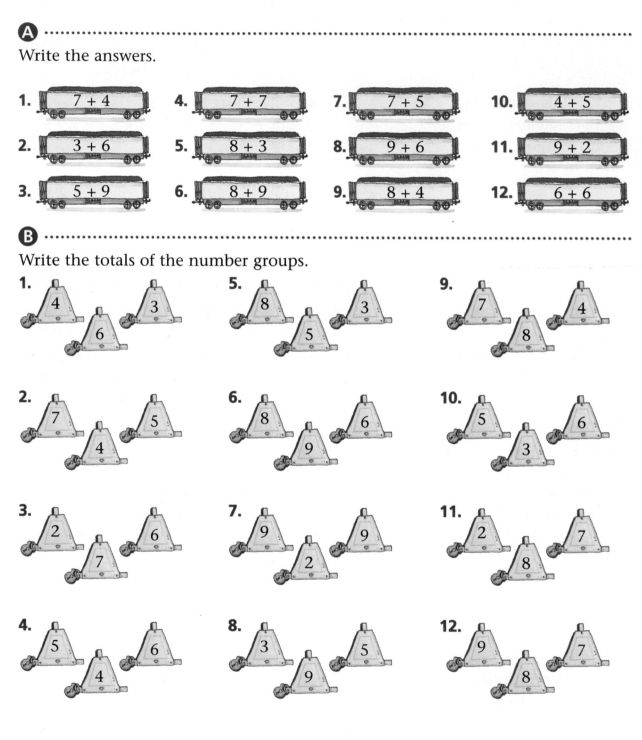

1. 4 6 3

2. 7 4 5

3. 2 7 6

4. 5 4 6

5. 8 5 3

6. 8 9 6

7. 9 2 9

8. 3 9 5

9. 7 8 4

10. 5 3 6

11. 2 8 7

12. 9 8 7

Addition Facts

C ....

Find the missing numbers.

1. 3 + ⬤ = 12   4. ⬤ + 7 = 13   7. ⬤ + 7 = 10   10. ⬤ + 6 = 11

2. ⬤ + 5 = 13   5. 9 + ⬤ = 13   8. 4 + ⬤ = 7   11. 6 + ⬤ = 14

3. 4 + ⬤ = 8   6. 8 + ⬤ = 16   9. ⬤ + 9 = 16   12. ⬤ + 9 = 18

D ....

Write the answers.

1. 15 + 8   6. 19 + 3   11. 5 + 15   16. 16 + 10   21. 11 + 14
2. 5 + 11   7. 7 + 18   12. 12 + 6   17. 11 + 12   22. 15 + 19
3. 17 + 4   8. 14 + 9   13. 4 + 13   18. 13 + 14   23. 18 + 17
4. 9 + 18   9. 6 + 16   14. 6 + 19   19. 16 + 17   24. 16 + 18
5. 12 + 7   10. 19 + 9   15. 17 + 7   20. 10 + 10   25. 18 + 19

E ....

Write the answers.

1. What is the sum of 14 and 6?   5. Add together 16 and 12.
2. Total 7 and 9.   6. What is the total of 6 and 19?
3. Add together 19 and 8.   7. Find the sum of 5 and 8.
4. What number is 5 more than 18?   8. What number is 7 more than 17?

Subtraction Facts

A

Write the answers.

1. 7 – 3	**4.** 18 – 11	**7.** 8 – 4	**10.** 13 – 5	**13.** 19 – 7
2. 10 – 6	**5.** 19 – 2	**8.** 15 – 6	**11.** 20 – 9	**14.** 15 – 9
3. 20 – 15	**6.** 14 – 7	**9.** 17 – 4	**12.** 16 – 12	**15.** 20 – 13

B

Find the missing numbers.

1. $14 - \square = 11$ **4.** $6 - \square = 2$ **7.** $13 - \square = 8$ **10.** $16 - \square = 9$

2. $20 - \square = 10$ **5.** $18 - \square = 3$ **8.** $20 - \square = 14$ **11.** $19 - \square = 8$

3. $19 - \square = 4$ **6.** $7 - \square = 4$ **9.** $11 - \square = 7$ **12.** $17 - \square = 8$

C

Write the difference between these pairs of numbers.

1. 11 3	**4.** 19 4	**7.** 9 5	**10.** 19 6
2. 17 7	**5.** 10 2	**8.** 15 3	**11.** 20 12
3. 20 6	**6.** 13 8	**9.** 12 9	**12.** 16 5

D

Copy and complete the tables.

→ In | –7 | Out →

IN	20	15	9	12
OUT				

→ In | –9 | Out →

IN				
OUT	3	10	5	9

E

Write the answers.

1. What is the difference between 20 and 11?

2. Subtract 4 from 12.

3. What is 7 less than 19?

4. Take 8 away from 14.

5. Subtract 7 from 19.

Multiplication Facts

A

Write the answers.

1. 5×6	**5.** 8×2	**9.** 7×4	**13.** 6×6	**17.** 3×4
2. 3×7	**6.** 9×5	**10.** 3×5	**14.** 8×9	**18.** 7×8
3. 4×4	**7.** 6×8	**11.** 3×9	**15.** 7×7	**19.** 4×6
4. 3×6	**8.** 9×7	**12.** 8×3	**16.** 5×5	**20.** 4×8

B

Copy and complete the sums.

1. △ $\times 4 = 20$	**5.** △ $\times 2 = 14$	**9.** $3 \times$ △ $= 9$	**13.** △ $\times 3 = 24$
2. $9 \times$ △ $= 63$	**6.** $8 \times$ △ $= 32$	**10.** △ $\times 4 = 36$	**14.** $8 \times$ △ $= 16$
3. $5 \times$ △ $= 25$	**7.** △ $\times 6 = 42$	**11.** △ $\times 9 = 54$	**15.** $9 \times$ △ $= 18$
4. $6 \times$ △ $= 12$	**8.** △ $\times 3 = 15$	**12.** $9 \times$ △ $= 27$	**16.** $7 \times$ △ $= 21$

C

Write the different facts for each number, e.g. $6 = 1 \times 6$
2×3

20	12	18	24
☐ × ☐	☐ × ☐	☐ × ☐	☐ × ☐
☐ × ☐	☐ × ☐	☐ × ☐	☐ × ☐
☐ × ☐	☐ × ☐	☐ × ☐	☐ × ☐
			☐ × ☐

26	28	32
☐ × ☐	☐ × ☐	☐ × ☐
☐ × ☐	☐ × ☐	☐ × ☐
☐ × ☐	☐ × ☐	☐ × ☐

Multiplication Facts

D ·····································

Write the answers.

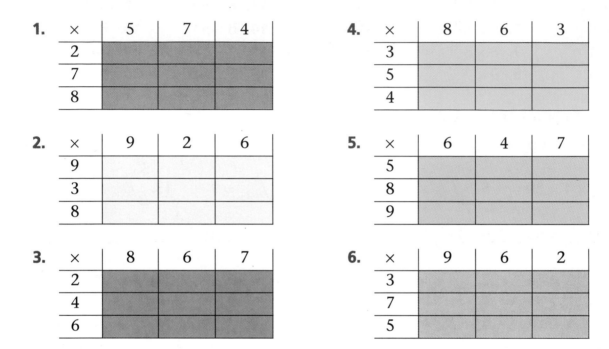

1.

×	5	7	4
2			
7			
8			

4.

×	8	6	3
3			
5			
4			

2.

×	9	2	6
9			
3			
8			

5.

×	6	4	7
5			
8			
9			

3.

×	8	6	7
2			
4			
6			

6.

×	9	6	2
3			
7			
5			

E ·····································

Write the answers.

1. What is 7 times 6?
2. Multiply 8 by 8.
3. What number is 9 times greater than 4?
4. Multiply 6 by 8.
5. Times 5 by 6.
6. Multiply 3 by 7.
7. What is 4 times greater than 2?
8. What is 6 times 4?
9. Times 7 by 5.

1.4

Division Facts

A

Write the answers.

1. 24 ÷ 6   4. 45 ÷ 9   7. 56 ÷ 8   10. 80 ÷ 8   13. 20 ÷ 4
2. 20 ÷ 5   5. 28 ÷ 7   8. 18 ÷ 2   11. 21 ÷ 3   14. 36 ÷ 6
3. 12 ÷ 3   6. 16 ÷ 4   9. 42 ÷ 6   12. 72 ÷ 9   15. 72 ÷ 8

B

Copy and complete the tables.

→ In | ÷6 | Out →

IN	48	60	18	24
OUT				

→ In | ÷6 | Out →

IN				
OUT	7	3	8	4

C

Copy and complete the sums.

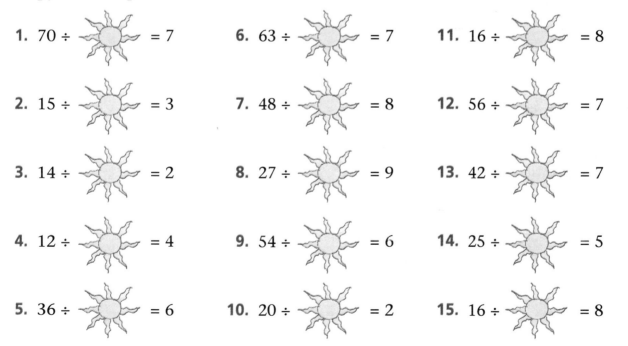

1. 70 ÷ ☼ = 7   6. 63 ÷ ☼ = 7   11. 16 ÷ ☼ = 8

2. 15 ÷ ☼ = 3   7. 48 ÷ ☼ = 8   12. 56 ÷ ☼ = 7

3. 14 ÷ ☼ = 2   8. 27 ÷ ☼ = 9   13. 42 ÷ ☼ = 7

4. 12 ÷ ☼ = 4   9. 54 ÷ ☼ = 6   14. 25 ÷ ☼ = 5

5. 36 ÷ ☼ = 6   10. 20 ÷ ☼ = 2   15. 16 ÷ ☼ = 8

Division Facts

D ....

Divide each of these numbers by 4. Divide each of these numbers by 7.

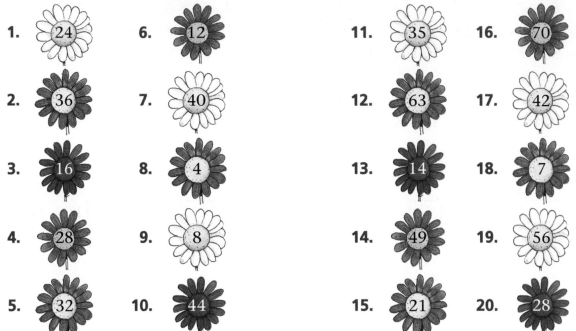

1. 24
2. 36
3. 16
4. 28
5. 32
6. 12
7. 40
8. 4
9. 8
10. 44

11. 35
12. 63
13. 14
14. 49
15. 21
16. 70
17. 42
18. 7
19. 56
20. 28

E ....

Write the answer.
1. What is 54 shared equally by 9?
2. Divide 40 by 8.
3. How many times does 7 go into 63?
4. Share 36 equally between 6.
5. Share 35 equally between 5.
6. Divide 49 by 7.
7. Share 48 equally between 8.
8. How many times does 9 go into 63?
9. Divide 32 by 4.
10. Share 64 equally between 8.

Using Brackets

A ....

Write the answers.

1. $(8 + 2) \times 4$
2. $(17 - 5) \div 3$
3. $18 - (4 \times 3)$
4. $(6 \times 4) \div 8$
5. $9 + (20 - 14)$

6. $7 \times (5 + 3)$
7. $(27 \div 3) \times 5$
8. $16 + (18 - 9)$
9. $56 \div (13 - 5)$
10. $(7 \times 4) - 10$

11. $(12 + 9) - 4$
12. $(64 \div 8) + 14$
13. $30 - (7 \times 3)$
14. $(4 \times 9) \div 6$
15. $16 + (4 \times 3)$

B ....

Write the answers.

1. $(4 + 3) \times (6 - 2)$
2. $(3 \times 4) + (14 \div 2)$
3. $(6 \times 6) \div (5 + 4)$
4. $(18 + 7) - (3 \times 3)$

5. $(8 \times 3) \div (17 - 13)$
6. $(42 \div 6) \times (5 + 3)$
7. $(4 \times 7) - (12 + 6)$
8. $(45 \div 5) + (30 - 12)$

9. $(17 + 9) - (54 \div 9)$
10. $(22 - 8) + (19 - 5)$
11. $(32 \div 4) \times (24 - 17)$
12. $(19 + 9) \div (21 \div 3)$

C ....

Copy these, putting the brackets in the correct place.

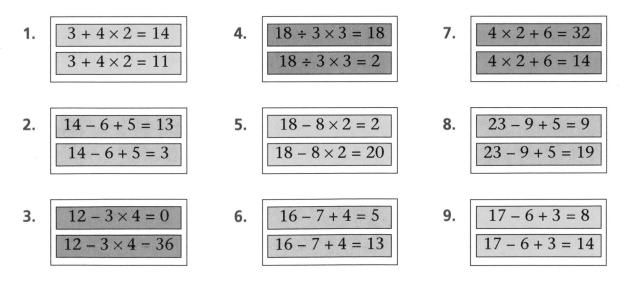

1. $3 + 4 \times 2 = 14$
   $3 + 4 \times 2 = 11$

4. $18 \div 3 \times 3 = 18$
   $18 \div 3 \times 3 = 2$

7. $4 \times 2 + 6 = 32$
   $4 \times 2 + 6 = 14$

2. $14 - 6 + 5 = 13$
   $14 - 6 + 5 = 3$

5. $18 - 8 \times 2 = 2$
   $18 - 8 \times 2 = 20$

8. $23 - 9 + 5 = 9$
   $23 - 9 + 5 = 19$

3. $12 - 3 \times 4 = 0$
   $12 - 3 \times 4 - 36$

6. $16 - 7 + 4 = 5$
   $16 - 7 + 4 = 13$

9. $17 - 6 + 3 = 8$
   $17 - 6 + 3 = 14$

Using Brackets

··

Write the answers.

1. $(4 + 3) \times (6 - 2)$
2. $5 \times (63 \div 9)$
3. $(4 \times 9) \div (14 - 8)$
4. $(17 + 8) - 11$
5. $(56 \div 7) + 18$
6. $(15 + 9) - (8 \times 3)$

7. $(26 - 7) - (5 \times 3)$
8. $(23 + 7) \div 6$
9. $6 \times (16 \div 2)$
10. $(13 + 8) - (4 + 6)$
11. $(54 \div 9) \times (16 - 9)$
12. $17 + (12 - 5)$

13. $(4 + 5) \times 5$
14. $14 + (48 \div 6)$
15. $(17 - 9) + 15$
16. $(3 \times 4) + (16 - 8)$
17. $(6 \times 5) - (2 \times 3)$
18. $19 - (4 \times 3)$

E ···

Write the answers.

1. Add together 3 and 5 and multiply the answer by 4.
2. Divide 49 by 7 and then add 16.
3. What number is 6 less than 3 multiplied by 8?
4. Subtract 5 from 29 and share the answer equally between 6.
5. Divide 64 by 8 and then add 12.
6. What number is 4 less than 5 multiplied by 2?
7. Subtract 6 from 27 and share the answer equally between 7.
8. Divide 36 by 6 and add 11.

9. What number is 4 less than 9 times 2.
10. Add together 4 and 4 and multiply the answer by 3.
11. Divide 35 by 7 and then add 18.
12. What number is 9 less than 6 multiplied by 4?
13. Take 11 away from 19 and add 17.
14. Subtract 5 from 25 and share the answer equally by 2.
15. Add together 5 and 4 and multiply by 9.
16. Divide 35 by 5.

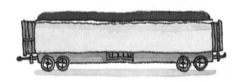

Summary for Unit 1

A ....

Write the answers.

1. 6 + 8
2. 9 + 3
3. 14 + 7

4. 25 + 9
5. 17 + 6
6. 9 + 8

7. 18p + 4p
8. 6p + 8p
9. 5p + 26p

10. 9p + 7p
11. 4p + 15p
12. 18p + 8p

B ....

Write the difference between the pairs of numbers.

1. 3   10
2. 5   12

3. 19   6
4. 17   9

5. 15   4
6. 9   18

Write the answers.

7. What is 6 less than 13?
8. Subtract 11 from 16.

9. Take 7 away from 15.
10. What is 19 take away 13?

C ....

Copy and complete these tables.

1.

×	4	8	3
5			
3			
6			

3.

×	7	2	6
9			
4			
7			

D ....

Copy and complete these tables.

→ In | −7 | Out →

IN	24	16	32	20
OUT				

→ In | −8 | Out →

IN	21	42	63	14
OUT				

→ In | −9 | Out →

IN	36	54	27	72
OUT				

Knowledge needed
- ✓ knows about digits
- ✓ multiplication and division by 10

Helpful facts

Digits
There are ten digits   0, 1, 2, 3, 4, 5, 6, 7, 8, 9

4-digit numbers
All the whole numbers from 1000 to 9999:

thousands   hundreds   tens   units

$$4 \quad 1 \quad 6 \quad 3 \qquad 4000 + 100 + 60 + 3$$

Spike abacus

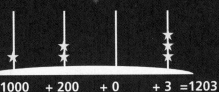

thousands   hundreds   tens   units   1000   + 200   + 0   + 3 =1203

Thousands

hundred thousands	ten thousands	thousands	hundreds	tens	units

A shorthand way of writing a thousand is to use k:

3000 = 3k   50,000 = 50k

Commas are sometimes used to separate thousands from hundreds: 3425   86,205   159,238

Rounding

examples

To the nearest 10:
look at the last digit; if less than 5 round down, otherwise round up:

83 round down 80
708 round up 710
1235 round up 1240

To the nearest 100:
look at last two digits; if less than 50 round down, otherwise round up:

742 round down 700
1670 round up 1700
27,450 round up 27,500

To the nearest 1000:
look at the last 3 digits; if less than 500 round down, otherwise round up:

62,489 round down 62,000
4870 round up 5000
13,500 round up 14,000

Multiplying and dividing by 10 and 100

Multiplying by 10:
move the digits 1 place to the left
and fill the space with a zero

Multiplying by 100:
move the digits 2 places to the left
and fill the spaces with two zeros

Dividing by 10:
move the digits 1 place to the right

Dividing by 100:
move the digits 2 places to the right

Learning outcomes for UNIT 2

reads and writes numbers to at least 100,000
knows the value of digits in 5-digit numbers
multiplies and divides whole numbers by 10 and 100
rounds a 3- or 4-digit number to the nearest 10, 100 or 1000
approximates the value of numbers to the nearest 10, 100 and 1000
orders a mixed set of whole numbers
uses place value in the context of measures

2.1

Reading and Writing Numbers Beyond 10,000

A ....

Write these numbers using digits.

1. Twelve thousand.
2. Fourteen thousand one hundred and eighty.
3. Thirty thousand and fifty-two.
4. Sixty-seven thousand four hundred and eighty-one.
5. Forty-three thousand nine hundred and six.
6. Sixteen thousand two hundred and ninety-three.
7. Eighty thousand six hundred and eleven.
8. Ninety-four thousand and twenty-eight.
9. Sixteen thousand and three.
10. Thirteen thousand and twenty.

B ....

Write these numbers using words.

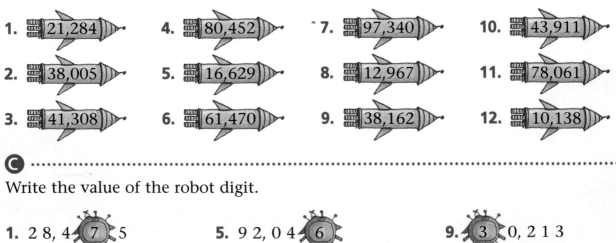

1. 21,284
2. 38,005
3. 41,308
4. 80,452
5. 16,629
6. 61,470
7. 97,340
8. 12,967
9. 38,162
10. 43,911
11. 78,061
12. 10,138

C ....

Write the value of the robot digit.

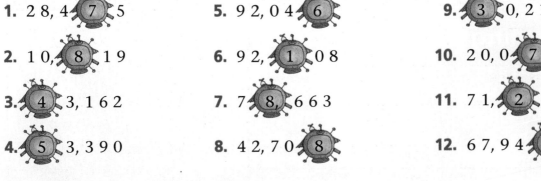

1. 2 8, 4 **7** 5
2. 1 0, **8** 1 9
3. **4** 3, 1 6 2
4. **5** 3, 3 9 0
5. 9 2, 0 4 **6**
6. 9 2, **1** 0 8
7. 7 **8**, 6 6 3
8. 4 2, 7 0 **8**
9. **3** 0, 2 1 3
10. 2 0, 0 **7** 9
11. 7 1, **2** 8 9
12. 6 7, 9 4 **0**

Reading and Writing Numbers Beyond 10,000

D

Write the number shown on each abacus.

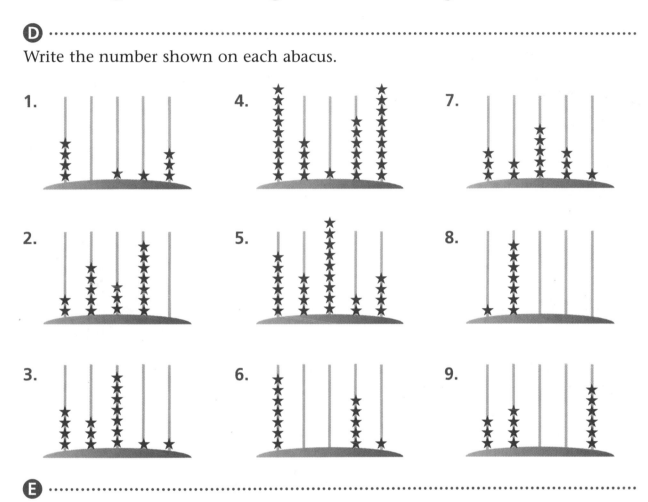

1.

2.

3.

4.

5.

6.

7.

8.

9.

E

Write the numbers using words.

The most common types of lost property on London Transport				
	1986–7		1991–2	
	Number of items	Number of items in words	Number of items	Number of items in words
Books, cheque books and credit cards	19,013		20,436	
Value items (handbags, purses, wallets)	21,940		17,342	
Clothing	16,497		13,704	
Umbrellas	21,080		10,917	

Multiplying and Dividing by 10 and 100

A

Multiply each of these numbers by 10.

1. 287   **6.** 503   **11.** 1123   **16.** 344

2. 495   **7.** 6284   **12.** 7014   **17.** 891

3. 610   **8.** 9020   **13.** 700   **18.** 4300

4. 308   **9.** 6408   **14.** 4066   **19.** 613

5. 101   **10.** 3296   **15.** 9114   **20.** 5720

B

Multiply each of these numbers by 100.

1. 48   **6.** 50   **11.** 864   **16.** 87
2. 96   **7.** 325   **12.** 599   **17.** 600
3. 17   **8.** 130   **13.** 201   **18.** 452
4. 24   **9.** 218   **14.** 398   **19.** 613
5. 35   **10.** 642 **15.** 9114   **20.** 5720

C

Divide each of these numbers by 10.

1. 6820   **6.** 5740   **11.** 67,820   **16.** 18,430
2. 5010   **7.** 38,820 **12.** 10,060   **17.** 4000
3. 9200   **8.** 47,600 **13.** 2950   **18.** 96,810
4. 260   **9.** 6490   **14.** 10,620   **19.** 460
5. 390   **10.** 5860 **15.** 3980   **20.** 32,090

Multiplying and Dividing by 10 and 100

D ....

Divide each of these numbers by 100.

1. 3800   6. 9700   11. 10,300   16. 27,300

2. 6300   7. 21,500   12. 34,000   17. 80,000

3. 4000   8. 58,900   13. 5600   18. 2700

4. 6900   9. 57,600   14. 4200   19. 30,600

5. 3600   10. 10,600   15. 2000   20. 29,400

E ....

Write the missing numbers.

→ In | ×10 | Out →

IN	6128		190		571
OUT		2540		78,000	

→ In | ×100 | Out →

IN		412	95		
OUT	3200			18,200	4000

Ordering Numbers to 99,999

A

Write these numbers in order of size starting with the smallest number.

1.	4362	90,156	10,067	6410	8000
2.	25,874	83,000	1207	68,200	5728

B

Write these numbers in order of size starting with the largest.

1.	47,001	1070	1047	70,410	1740
2.	14,470	7140	71,400	4007	4701

C

Write the middle number.

1. 3756 _____ 3758   **4.** 8499 _____ 8501   **7.** 67,080 _____ 67,082

2. 60,070 _____ 60,072   **5.** 71,621 _____ 71,623   **8.** 61,999 _____ 62,001

3. 2998 _____ 3000   **6.** 40,386 _____ 40,388   **9.** 18,399 _____ 18,401

D

Make as many numbers as you can using all the digits. Write the numbers in order, with the smallest first.

1. 6 2 1 3

2. 5 0 8 7 9

E

Rearrange the table so that the mountains are in size order, largest first.

Mountain heights			
Mountain	**Height in metres**	**Mountain**	**Height in metres**
Kirkpatrick (Antarctica)	4288	Kosciusko (Australia)	2230
Etna (Italy)	3233	Santa Marta (Colombia)	5873
St. Elias (Canada)	5489	Dom (Switzerland)	4544
Meru (Tanzania)	4566		

2.4

Estimating and Rounding

A

Round these numbers to the nearest 10.

1. 11   **3.** 34   **5.** 197   **7.** 6608   **9.** 29,317

2. 459   **4.** 892   **6.** 3855   **8.** 7002   **10.** 75,023

B

Estimate the number each arrow points to.

1000   **1.**   **2.**   **3.**   **4.**   2000

54,000   **5.**   **6.**   **7.**   **8.** 55,000

C

Round these numbers to the nearest 100.

1. 506   **3.** 1491   **5.** 6952   **7.** 93,108   **9.** 5998

2. 279   **4.** 834   **6.** 2849   **8.** 45,023   **10.** 85,256

D

Estimate the number each arrow points to.

30,000   **1.**   **2.**   **3.**   **4.**   40,000

54,000   **5.**   **6.**   **7.**   **8.**   55,000

E

Round these areas to the nearest 1000 square kilometre.

Country	Area in sq kms	Country	Area in sq kms
Jamaica	11,425	Hungary	93,030
Switzerland	41,285	The Gambia	10,690
Denmark	43,075	Cyprus	9250

Measures

A

Write the missing numbers.

1. 700 cm = ☐ m
2. 2300 cm = ☐ m
3. 38,000 m = ☐ km

4. 340 mm = ☐ cm
5. 51,000 m = ☐ km
6. 800 cm = ☐ m

7. 120 mm = ☐ cm
8. 2000 cm = ☐ m
9. 550 mm = ☐ cm

B

Write the missing numbers.

1. 48,000 g = ☐ kg
2. 6000 g = ☐ kg
3. 21,000 g = ☐ kg

4. 7000 g = ☐ kg
5. 5000 m*l* = ☐ *l*
6. 93,000 m*l* = ☐ *l*

7. 30,000 m*l* = ☐ *l*
8. 8000 m*l* = ☐ *l*
9. 240 g = ☐ kg

C

Write the missing numbers.

1. 24 km = ☐ m
2. 37 *l* = ☐ m*l*
3. 45 cm = ☐ mm

4. 6 kg = ☐ g
5. 50 m = ☐ cm
6. 3 cm = ☐ mm

7. 16 m = ☐ cm
8. 350 cm = ☐ mm
9. 24 m = ☐ mm

D

Write these lengths in order, starting with the shortest.

1.	75 km	3200 cm	9000 m	480 m
2.	8 km	46,000 mm	87,000 m	24,000 cm

E

Round each of these using sensible approximations.

1. Karen Brown travelled a total of 92,743 km.
2. Sam weighs 28,392 g.
3. A farm container holds 62,949 litres of milk.
4. The width of the play area is 8439 cm.

Summary for Unit 2

A

Write these using numerals.

1. Fifteen thousand four hundred and two.
2. Twenty thousand and thirty-eight.
3. Forty-two thousand six hundred and twelve.
4. Eighty-nine thousand five hundred and seventy.
5. Eleven thousand three hundred and ninety-one.
6. Sixty-three thousand seven hundred and fifty.

Write these using words.
7. 48,371
8. 10,680
9. 82,319
10. 91,045
11. 53,406
12. 74,001

B

Write the missing numbers.

→ In | ×10 | Out →

IN	635		29		450
OUT		740		5920	

→ In | ×100 | Out →

IN		418		87	
OUT	3800		19,700		80,000

C

Estimate the number each arrow points to.

25,000 1. 2. 3. 4. 35,000

D

Round these numbers to the nearest 100 or 1000.

1. 942   2. 3059   3. 14,760   4. 502   5. 7249   6. 9958

E

Write these lengths in order, starting with the smallest.

5730 mm	56200 m	600 m	5000 m	56410 mm
50000 mm	5700 cm	506 km	5300 cm	72 km

Knowledge needed
✓ efficient use of addition facts to 20
✓ knowledge of place value

Helpful facts

Addition can be done in any order

It does not matter in which order you add numbers. Choose the order you find easiest:

examples

$13 + 29 = 29 + 13$

$45 + 93 = 93 + 45$

Knowing doubles

Knowing doubles can help you find other totals:

examples

$50 + 50 = 100$

$51 + 53 = 104$

$46 + 46 = 92$

$46 + 47 = 93$

Addition and subtraction are opposites

An addition sum can be checked by subtracting:

$58 + 46 = 104$

$104 - 46 = 58$

Quick methods

Adding 9:
add 10 subtract 1

$74 + 9 = 83$

Adding 19:
add 20 subtract 1

$112 + 19 = 131$

Adding 99:
add 100 subtract 1

$253 + 99 = 352$

Adding 999:
add 1000 subtract 1

$8456 + 999 = 9455$

Adding the tens then the units

When adding TU numbers, try holding
the first number in your head and
then adding the tens and the units:

$47 + 36$
$47 + 30 = 77$
$77 + 6 = 83$

Breaking up numbers can help add mentally

4   9 + 3   7   add the tens then
↓   ↓   ↓   ↓   add the units:
$(40 + 9) + (30 + 7)$ $70 + 16 = 86$

Adding the nearest decade number and adjusting

$56 + 79$
$56 + [80$ then $- 1] = 135$
$64 + 52$
$64 + [50$ then $+ 2] = 116$

Learning outcomes for UNIT 3

✓ uses a range of mental methods for addition
✓ mentally adds any two 2-digit numbers
✓ uses the relationship between addition and subtraction
✓ uses knowledge of addition facts and place value to add any 3-digit numbers
✓ finds the total of three 2-digit numbers
✓ solves addition word problems

Addition of TU and TU

Complete these sums and check your answers.

1. 40 + 30   3. 30 + 50   5. 50 + 40   7. 60 + 70   9. 30 + 70
2. 20 + 60   4. 70 + 20   6. 80 + 40   8. 90 + 50   10. 60 + 80

A

Add these number pairs.

1. 23   41   4. 57   31   7. 12   85   10. 52   30
2. 34   35   5. 70   13   8. 23   23   11. 46   53
3. 16   62   6. 25   63   9. 14   14   12. 25   63

B

Write the total price.

1. 45p 45p   4. 53p 29p   7. 54p 19p   10. 37p 38p
2. 15p 76p   5. 25p 69p   8. 22p 29p   11. 49p 29p
3. 36p 48p   6. 67p 23p   9. 15p 67p   12. 35p 48p

C

Copy and complete these grids. Add together the rows, then the columns.

1.
75	42	
56	67	

2.
64	59	
86	93	

3.
49	79	
97	93	

D

Write the answers.

1. Drinks cost 25p and burgers cost 58p. What is the total cost of one burger and one drink?
2. What number is 76 more than 34?
3. Add together 68 and 93.
4. What is the sum of 87 and 49?

3.2

Addition of TU and TU and TU

Key Skills ✓

Complete these sums and check your answers.

1. 3 + 4 + 7
2. 8 + 1 + 9
3. 5 + 6 + 2
4. 7 + 7 + 4
5. 8 + 5 + 4
6. 2 + 9 + 3
7. 4 + 6 + 1
8. 7 + 9 + 4
9. 3 + 3 + 6
10. 6 + 8 + 3
11. 7 + 3 + 8
12. 9 + 5 + 6
13. 7 + 6 + 8
14. 3 + 7 + 5
15. 8 + 6 + 8

A

Total these numbers.

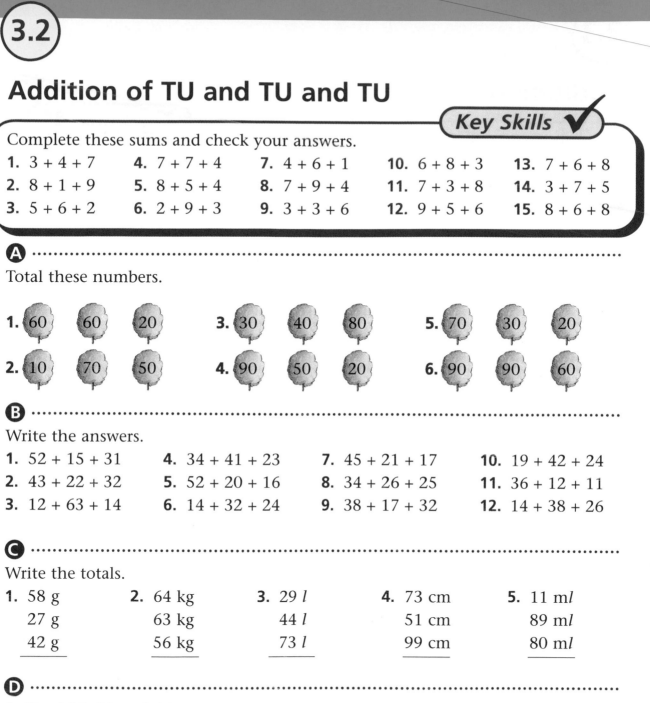

1. 60 60 20
2. 10 70 50
3. 30 40 80
4. 90 50 20
5. 70 30 20
6. 90 90 60

B

Write the answers.

1. 52 + 15 + 31
2. 43 + 22 + 32
3. 12 + 63 + 14
4. 34 + 41 + 23
5. 52 + 20 + 16
6. 14 + 32 + 24
7. 45 + 21 + 17
8. 34 + 26 + 25
9. 38 + 17 + 32
10. 19 + 42 + 24
11. 36 + 12 + 11
12. 14 + 38 + 26

C

Write the totals.

1. 58 g
   27 g
   42 g

2. 64 kg
   63 kg
   56 kg

3. 29 l
   44 l
   73 l

4. 73 cm
   51 cm
   99 cm

5. 11 ml
   89 ml
   80 ml

D

1. Total 37, 28 and 14.
2. Add together 54, 92 and 43.
3. David has 86 badges, Gita has 75 badges and Hannah has 49 badges.
   How many badges do they have altogether?
4. A recipe uses 25 g of butter, 75 g of flour and 50 g of sugar.
   How much will the ingredients weigh in total?

31

3.3

Addition of HTU and TU

Complete these sums and check your answers.

1. 24 + 3 **3.** 58 + 4 **5.** 96 + 9 **7.** 347 + 3 **9.** 683 + 8
2. 35 + 5 **4.** 67 + 7 **6.** 112 + 6 **8.** 209 + 5 **10.** 497 + 5

A

Copy and complete these tables.

1.

+ 30	
127	
238	
660	
372	

2.

+ 40	
547	
926	
759	
180	

3.

+ 80	
415	
394	
803	
576	

B

Write the answers.

1. 463 + 34 **3.** 924 + 44 **5.** 827 + 13 **7.** 749 + 39 **9.** 682 + 56
2. 152 + 16 **4.** 206 + 53 **6.** 365 + 26 **8.** 518 + 33 **10.** 352 + 63

C

Add the number pairs.

1. 39 167   **3.** 849 62   **5.** 377 52   **7.** 149 66
2. 528 54   **4.** 18 796   **6.** 27 836   **8.** 253 98

D

1. A photo album has 144 photos. There is space for another 24 photos. How many photos can this album hold in total?
2. What is the sum of 538 and 56?
3. What number is 93 more than 172?
4. There are 178 children in a school. 27 new children for next year come for a day visit. How many children will there be altogether in the school on this day?

3.4

Addition of HTU and HTU

Complete these sums and check your answers.

1. 300 + 400
2. 700 + 200
3. 500 + 300
4. 400 + 400
5. 200 + 300
6. 800 + 700
7. 900 + 300
8. 600 + 800
9. 500 + 700
10. 900 + 900
11. 100 + 900
12. 400 + 900

A

Add the number pairs.

1. 411, 352
2. 360, 238
3. 145, 624
4. 312, 469
5. 503, 273

6. 152, 732
7. 403, 494
8. 218, 646
9. 245, 614
10. 364, 532

11. 123, 456
12. 108, 592
13. 734, 235
14. 318, 570
15. 193, 104

B

Copy and complete the sums.

1. 275
   + 315

2. 838
   + 124

3. 402
   + 469

4. 364
   + 426

5. 619
   + 256

6. 124
   + 756

7. 546
   + 308

8. 108
   + 612

9. 551
   + 256

10. 184
    + 645

11. 760
    + 159

12. 681
    + 111

13. 233
    + 393

14. 492
    + 376

15. 527
    + 291

16. 264
    + 352

Addition of HTU and HTU

C ....

Copy and complete these sums.

1. 693 + 227	**4.** 382 + 488	**7.** 472 + 604	**10.** 764 + 994
2. 175 + 678	**5.** 237 + 395	**8.** 913 + 565	**11.** 359 + 782
3. 404 + 296	**6.** 598 + 165	**9.** 685 + 821	**12.** 877 + 467

D ....

1. A lorry travels 143 km one day and 225 km the next day.
   How many kilometres did the lorry travel in total on these two days?
2. Class 4 have collected 307 empty cans for recycling and Class 5 have collected
   284 cans. How many cans have they collected altogether?
3. What is the sum of 467 and 296?
4. Total 855 and 628.
5. Mr and Mrs Harris drive to the supermarket, which is 7 kilometres away. Then
   they visit Mrs Harris' mother who lives 15 kilometres from the supermarket.
   They take her for a drive in the country for 13 kilometres before going home.
   How far have Mr and Mrs Harris travelled in total?
6. Total 855 and 628.

3.5

Adding Three Numbers

Complete these sums and check your answers.

1. 13 + 8 + 6
2. 7 + 18 + 9
3. 9 + 4 + 15
4. 5 + 8 + 17
5. 6 + 19 + 9
6. 14 + 3 + 8
7. 6 + 7 + 16
8. 11 + 8 + 8
9. 26 + 4 + 7
10. 8 + 25 + 5
11. 9 + 3 + 21
12. 27 + 7 + 4

A

1. 347 + 28 + 456
2. 74 + 193 + 6
3. 52 + 79 + 45
4. 204 + 560 + 88
5. 791 + 9 + 17
6. 236 + 86 + 12
7. 59 + 732 + 185
8. 67 + 484 + 39

B

Write the missing 3-digit numbers to make each total 500.

1. 284 + 68 + ☐☐☐
2. 94 + 221 + ☐☐☐
3. 145 + 253 + ☐☐☐
4. 76 + 199 + ☐☐☐
5. 9 + 303 + ☐☐☐
6. 59 + 240 + ☐☐☐
7. 158 + 174 + ☐☐☐
8. 226 + 97 + ☐☐☐
9. 24 + 290 + ☐☐☐

C

1. Which three numbers total 500?
2. What is the sum of the odd numbers?
3. What is the sum of the even numbers?
4. Which pairs of numbers total 293?
5. What is the largest possible total using only three of the numbers?
6. What is the smallest possible total using only three of the numbers?

246   47   184   65   207   86

D

Month	January	February	March	April	May	June
Km travelled	618	803	714	897	906	628

1. What was the total distance travelled in the first three months?
2. What was the total distance travelled in the last three months?
3. Find the three months that have the greatest distances. What is the total distance travelled in these three months?
4. Find the three months that have the smallest distances. What is the total distance travelled in these three months?

3.6

Mixed Sums

Complete these sums and check your answers.

1. 30 + 40 + 80
2. 70 + 50
3. 60 + 20 + 30 + 20
4. 90 + 90

5. 40 + 50
6. 90 + 30 + 50
7. 70 + 40 + 60
8. 80 + 30 + 50 + 60

9. 40 + 90 + 70 + 20
10. 60 + 80
11. 10 + 60 + 30 + 50
12. 40 + 80 + 40

A ....

Copy and complete these grids.
Add together the rows, then the columns.

1.

268	29	384	
64	91	217	
302	28	194	

2.

108	419	75	
293	182	37	
46	209	58	

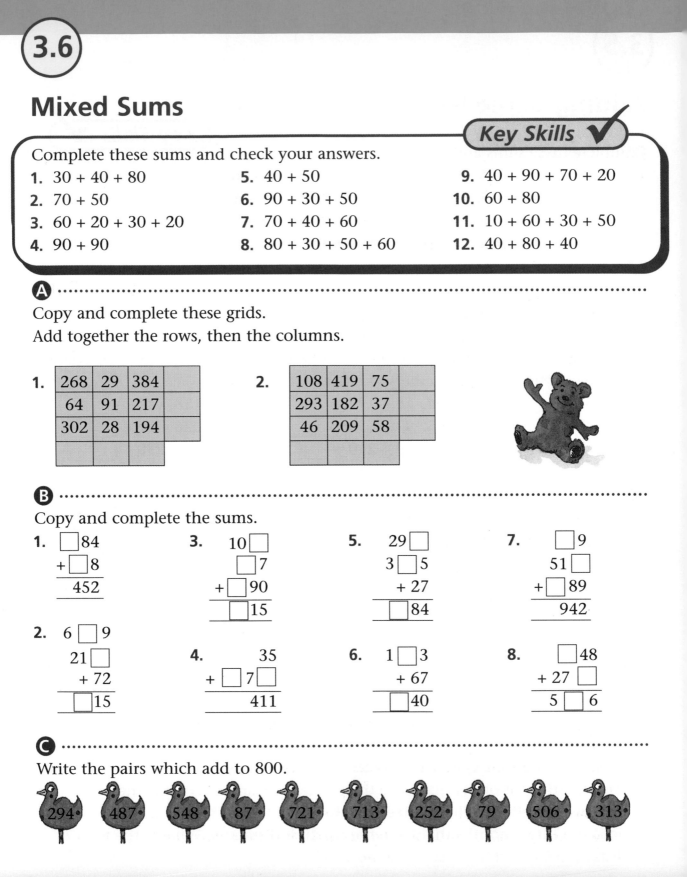

B ....

Copy and complete the sums.

1.
```
  □84
+ □8
─────
 452
```

2.
```
  6□9
  21□
+ 72
─────
 □15
```

3.
```
  10□
   □7
+ □90
─────
  □15
```

4.
```
     35
+ □7□
─────
   411
```

5.
```
  29□
  3□5
+ 27
─────
 □84
```

6.
```
  1□3
+ 67
─────
 □40
```

7.
```
   □9
  51□
+ □89
─────
  942
```

8.
```
  □48
+ 27□
─────
 5□6
```

C ....

Write the pairs which add to 800.

294 •   487 •   548 •   87 •   721 •   713 •   252 •   79 •   506 •   313 •

3.7

Addition Problems

A
Write the answers.

1. David reads 19 pages of his book on Saturday and 34 more pages on Sunday.
   How many pages did he read in total on Saturday and Sunday?
2. Hannah buys a ruler for 46p and a pencil for 27p.
   How much does she spend altogether?
3. A coach travels 39 km from Leeds to York and then 62 km from York to Hull.
   How many kilometres does the coach travel in total?
4. Gita has 68 marbles and Sam has 55 marbles.
   How many marbles do they have altogether?
5. A recipe uses 75 g of carrots and 90 g of onion.
   How much do these ingredients weigh in total?
6. Mrs Byers buys a coat for £86 and a pair of shoes for £59.
   How much does she spend in total?

B
These are the numbers of children who require a cooked school dinner each day.
Copy and complete the table.

	Monday	Tuesday	Wednesday	Thursday	Friday
Class 1	26	23	27	21	19
Class 2	18	22	17	19	20
Class 3	24	28	30	25	27
Total meals each day					

1. On Mondays, Wednesdays and Fridays each child has an apple.
   How many apples are needed in total?
2. How many school dinners were cooked in total on Wednesday,
   Thursday and Friday?
3. On Mondays, Tuesdays and Thursdays each child has a glass of milk.
   How many glasses of milk will be needed for these three days?

Addition Problems

Write the total weight of each pair.

1. 89 g 215 g   **3.** 68 g 726 g   **5.** 51 g 389 g   **7.** 703 g 38 g

2. 437 g 92 g   **4.** 544 g 76 g   **6.** 48 g 815 g   **8.** 64 g 357 g

D

Write the answers.

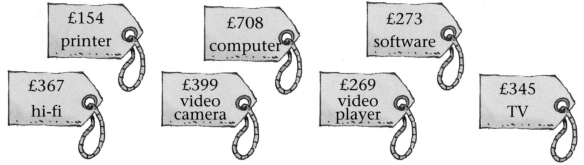

£154 printer

£708 computer

£273 software

£367 hi-fi

£399 video camera

£269 video player

£345 TV

How much would it cost to buy the following:

1. Computer and printer?   **4.** Hi-fi and TV?

2. TV and video player?   **5.** Video camera and hi-fi?

3. Video camera and video player? **6.** Computer and software?

E

Write the answers.

1. Ali swam 75 m and then 150 m. How far did he swim altogether?

2. Lucy's father is 36. His mother, Lucy's grandmother is 27 years older than him. Lucy's great-grandmother is 19 years older than her grandmother. How old is Lucy's great-grandmother?

3. A cinema sells 267 tickets on Saturday and 249 tickets on Sunday. How many tickets are sold in total?

4. Football boots cost £34 and a football cost £16. How much do they cost together?

Summary for Unit 3

A ··

Copy and complete these grids. Add the rows, then add the columns.

1.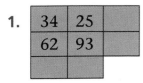

2.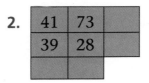

3.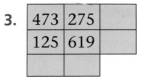

B ··

Write the answers.

1. 31 + 24 + 13   **4.** 19 + 42 + 54   **7.** 24 + 27 + 45   **10.** 92 + 13 + 77

2. 52 + 44 + 82   **5.** 27 + 15 + 49   **8.** 50 + 39 + 11   **11.** 58 + 26 + 97

3. 71 + 65 + 43   **6.** 38 + 18 + 36   **9.** 63 + 28 + 84   **12.** 89 + 56 + 74

C ··

Write the answers.

1. What is the sum of 35 and 128?

2. Total 634 and 46.

3. Add together 582 and 53.

4. What number is 68 more than 470?

5. Add 89 and 361.

6. Total 769 and 48.

7. Imran swims 280 m; Ryan swims 76 m further. How far does Ryan swim?

8. Two parcels weigh 87 g and 174 g. How much do they weigh together?

D ··

 63   258   24   466   179   305

1. What is the total of the odd numbers?

2. What is the total of the even numbers?

3. Which two numbers total 484?

4. Which three numbers total 500?

5. What is the largest possible total using three numbers?

6. What is the smallest possible total using four numbers?

Helpful facts

Quick methods
Subtracting 9:
subtract 10 add 1   73 − 9 = 64

Subtracting 99:
subtract 100 add 1   481 − 99 = 382

Subtracting 19:
subtract 20 add 1   137 − 19 = 118

Difference
To find the difference   64   97
between two numbers,   97 − 64 = 33
subtract them: ↗
                              difference

Subtraction and addition are opposites
A subtraction sum can   86 − 38 = 48
be checked by adding: 48 + 38 = 86

Brackets

When brackets are used, work out the sum in the brackets first:

$$47 - (4 \times 7)$$

↑ work out first $\quad 47 - 28 = 19$

Subtracting the nearest decade and adjusting

93 – 48

93 – [50 then + 2] = 45

81 – 44

81 – [40 then – 4] = 37

When subtracting, mentally count on using the 'shopkeepers' method'

93 – 58

Count on from 58 to 60 (hold 2 in your head)

Count on from 60 to 90 (hold 30 in your head)

Count on from 90 to 93 (add together 2, 30 and 3)

The answer to 93 – 58 is 35

Breaking up numbers can help to subtract mentally

78 – 46

78 – 40 + 6

= 38 – 6 = 32

When subtracting close numbers, count on or back

423 – 418

count on from 418

or count back from 423

The answer is 5

Learning outcomes for UNIT 4

✓ mentally subtracts any two 2-digit numbers

✓ uses knowledge of subtraction facts and place value to subtract any 3-digit numbers

✓ solves subtraction word problems

✓ uses a range of mental methods for subtraction

✓ uses the relationship between addition and subtraction

✓ finds the difference between two 2-digit numbers

Subtraction of TU and TU

Complete these sums and check your answers.

1. 80 – 20
2. 70 – 40
3. 90 – 60
4. 60 – 30
5. 90 – 50
6. 50 – 30
7. 80 – 40
8. 90 – 40
9. 70 – 20
10. 90 – 70
11. 80 – 50
12. 100 – 50

A

Write the answers.

1. 62 – 40
2. 75 – 30
3. 84 – 70
4. 46 – 20
5. 99 – 30
6. 89 – 60
7. 71 – 50
8. 96 – 10
9. 73 – 60
10. 58 – 20
11. 87 – 30
12. 72 – 30

B

Find the difference between these pairs of numbers.

1.	68	24
2.	59	35
3.	27	88
4.	12	46
5.	95	63
6.	41	77
7.	49	16
8.	97	34
9.	22	57
10.	85	53
11.	68	34
12.	79	37

C

Write the answers.

1. 58 – 29
2. 31 – 17
3. 64 – 38
4. 82 – 53
5. 95 – 67
6. 73 – 48
7. 49 – 29
8. 50 – 36
9. 71 – 45
10. 92 – 47
11. 66 – 57
12. 84 – 39

D

Write the change from £1 for each of these.

1. 87p
2. 29p
3. 51p
4. 60p
5. 42p
6. 38p
7. 14p
8. 93p
9. 75p
10. 67p

4.2

Subtraction of HTU and TU

Complete these sums and check your answers.
1. 34 – 8   3. 41 – 6   5. 72 – 5   7. 16 – 8   9. 62 – 6
2. 26 – 9   4. 57 – 8   6. 65 – 7   8. 83 – 4   10. 94 – 9

A

Copy and complete these tables.

1.

– 40	
257	
373	
126	
934	

2.

– 70	
189	
245	
617	
964	

3.

– 50	
391	
408	
726	
849	

B

Write the answers.
1. 268 – 31   3. 947 – 24   5. 479 – 45   7. 757 – 83   9. 325 – 61
2. 584 – 53   4. 695 – 63   6. 416 – 25   8. 809 – 74   10. 838 – 55

C

Find the difference between these pairs.
1. 246   74   3. 127   43   5. 643   56   7. 954   77
2. 619   63   4. 558   64   6. 401   82   8. 522   98

D

Write the answers.
1. There are 342 oranges in a box. 19 oranges have to be thrown away. How many oranges are left?
2. Subtract 83 from 259.
3. What is 615 take away 67?
4. A can holds 330 m*l* of drink. 58 m*l* is poured out. How much drink is left in the can?

43

4.3

Subtraction of HTU and HTU

A

Find the difference between these pairs.

1. 246 130 3. 895 360 5. 420 759 7. 650 914 9. 230 426

2. 483 240 4. 540 971 6. 363 180 8. 708 390 10. 521 340

B

Write the answers.
1. 243 – 121
3. 518 – 404
5. 498 – 247
7. 584 – 256
9. 793 – 428
2. 859 – 635
4. 973 – 632
6. 671 – 349
8. 990 – 635
10. 472 – 266

C

Copy and complete these.

1. 384 – 193	3. 938 – 375	5. 568 + 284	7. 503 – 164	9. 826 – 378	11. 912 – 663

1.   384
  – 193

3.   938
  – 375

5.   568
  + 284

7.   503
  – 164

9.   826
  – 378

11.   912
  – 663

2.   756
  – 484

4.   605
  + 173

6.   843
  + 692

8.   745
  – 349

10.   490
  – 295

12.   634
  – 148

D

Write the answers.
1. Subtract 573 from 895.
2. What is 627 take away 352?
3. Two pieces of wood measure 463 cm and 198 cm.
   What is the difference in length between these
   two pieces of wood?
4. A bus travelled 704 km in total in one day.

It travelled 387 km in the morning. How far did it travel in the afternoon?

Mixed Sums

Complete these sums and check your answers.

1. 18 – 7
2. 13 – 9
3. 19 – 11
4. 15 – 9
5. 18 – 13
6. 16 – 9
7. 11 – 5
8. 17 – 14
9. 12 – 3
10. 14 – 8
11. 19 – 16
12. 13 – 5
13. 16 – 11
14. 15 – 7
15. 17 – 9

A ....

Subtract each of these numbers from 500.

1. 240
2. 74
3. 291
4. 420
5. 137
6. 42
7. 363
8. 180
9. 215
10. 109

B ....

Write the pairs of numbers that have a difference of 250.

37 642 287 961 103

76 353 398 711 326

C ....

The table shows the six longest Rivers in the UK. Write the answers.

River	km
Severn	354
Thames	346
Trent	298
Aire	259
Great Ouse	230
Wye	217

1. How much longer is the Severn than the Wye?
2. What is the difference in length between the Trent and the Great Ouse?
3. Which two rivers have a difference in length of 48 km.
4. Which river is 95 km shorter than the River Severn?
5. Which two rivers have the smallest difference in length?

(4.5)

Subtraction Problems

A

How much change would you get from 75p for each of the following:

1. 47p 3. 68p 5. 72p 7. 19p 9. 43p

2. 21p 4. 35p 6. 50p 8. 56p 10. 24p

B

1. Two parcels weigh 232 g together. One of the parcels weighs 80 g.
   How much does the other parcel weigh?
2. Paul is 146 cm tall. He is 19 cm taller than his friend Ryan. How tall is Ryan?
3. The price of a bicycle is £109, but in the sale it is £25 less.
   How much is the cost of the bicycle in the sale?
4. A box holds 245 oranges. Of these, 68 oranges have to be thrown away.
   How many oranges are there left?
5. Mrs Smith has £476 in her bank account. She takes out £180.
   How much is left in her account?
6. Imran has 37 conkers. He gives away 19 to his friends.
   How many conkers does Imran have left?

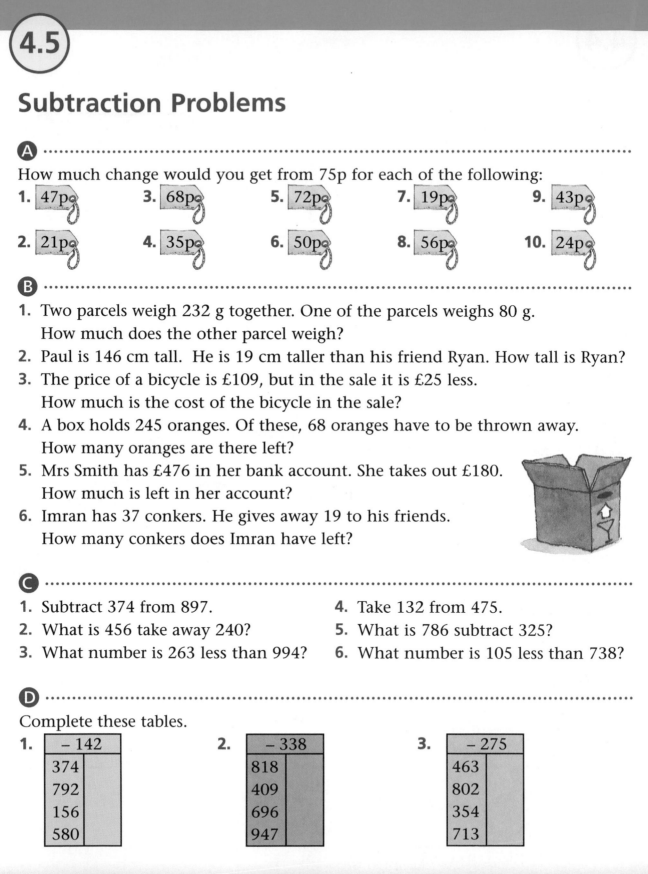

C

1. Subtract 374 from 897.
2. What is 456 take away 240?
3. What number is 263 less than 994?
4. Take 132 from 475.
5. What is 786 subtract 325?
6. What number is 105 less than 738?

D

Complete these tables.

1.

– 142	
374	
792	
156	
580	

2.

– 338	
818	
409	
696	
947	

3.

– 275	
463	
802	
354	
713	

Summary for Unit 4

A

Write the change from 75p for each of these.

1. 20p   **3.** 15p   **5.** 50p   **7.** 42p   **9.** 63p

2. 18p   **4.** 67p   **6.** 39p   **8.** 46p   **10.** 55p

B

1. What is 67 less than 289?

2. Subtract 52 from 165.

3. Alice has 214 badges. She has 67 more than Callum.
How many badges does Callum have?

4. Two parcels weigh 98 g and 350 g.
What is the difference in weight between these two parcels?

5. One packet of cereal weighs 545 g and another weighs 350 g.
What is the difference in weight between these two cereal packets?

6. Mrs Lake went to Buxton on holiday. On the way there she drove 213 km.
On her return journey she took a different route and drove 189 km.
How much shorter was the return journey?

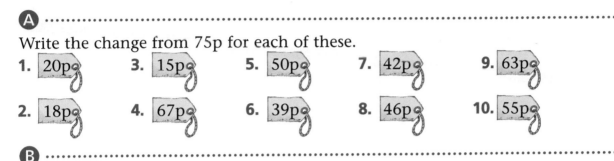

C

Complete these tables.

1.

− 340	
580	
972	
648	

2.

− 125	
679	
425	
850	

3.

− 827	
794	
507	
400	

D

Write the missing numbers.

→ In | − 64 | Out →

IN	576	739	468	801
OUT				

→ In | −273 | Out →

IN				
OUT	835	720	914	652

47

Knowledge needed
- ✓ recognising odd and even numbers
- ✓ recognising negative numbers
- ✓ quick recall of multiplication facts

Helpful facts

Multiples

The multiples of 3 are	3, 6, 9, 12, 15, ...
The multiples of 4 are	4, 12, 16, 20, 24, ...
Multiples of 2 are always even	2, 14, 16, 28, 30, 62, ...
Multiples of 5 always end in 5 or 0	15, 40, 65, 80, ...
Multiples of 10 always end in 0	10, 30, 140, 200, ...

Rules of divisibility

Whole numbers are divisible by:

10	if the last digit is 0	350, 2900, 6730, 2190 ....
5	if the last digit is 0 or 5	455, 260, 385, 205 ......
2	if the last digit is an even number	244, 8776, 3108, 2330 ....
3	if the sum of the digits is divisible by 3	81, 162, 255, 834 ......
4	if the last two digits are divisible by 4	144, 1328, 3640, 2076 .....
6	if it is even and also divisible by 3	126, 384, 1056, 3348 ....
8	if half of it is divisible by 4	144, 576, 440, 984 .....
9	if the sum of the digits is divisible by 9	324, 2052, 5787, 2907 .....

Factors

Factors are numbers which will divide exactly into other numbers.

The factors of 18 are	1, 2, 3, 6, 9 and 18
The factors of 30 are	1, 3, 5, 6, 10 and 30
5 is a factor of	5, 10, 15, 20, ...
7 is a factor of	7, 14, 21, 28, ...

Positive and negative numbers

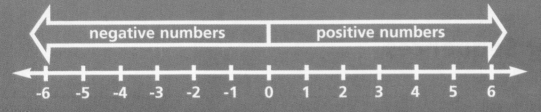

| negative numbers | positive numbers |

-6 -5 -4 -3 -2 -1 0 1 2 3 4 5 6

Prime numbers
Numbers which can only be divided by themselves and 1. Prime numbers up to 20 are 2, 3, 5, 7, 11, 13, 17, 19

Square root
To find the square root of a number, find a number that, when multiplied by itself, gives that number:
$\sqrt{49}$ 7 x 7 is 49   so $\sqrt{49} = 7$

Square numbers
To make a square number, multiply a number by itself:
3 x 3 = 9
9 is a square number
7 x 7 = 49
49 is a square number

Number sequences
When looking for a pattern in a sequence of numbers, look at the difference between consecutive numbers:

7   11   15   19   ...
  4   4   4   4

Learning outcomes for UNIT 5

✓ recognises and extends number sequences

✓ recognises squares of numbers to 10 x 10

✓ orders a set of negative numbers in context

✓ recognises multiples and knows tests of divisibility

✓ finds pairs of factors of any number up to 100

✓ calculates a temperature rise or fall across 0°C

5.1

Number Sequences

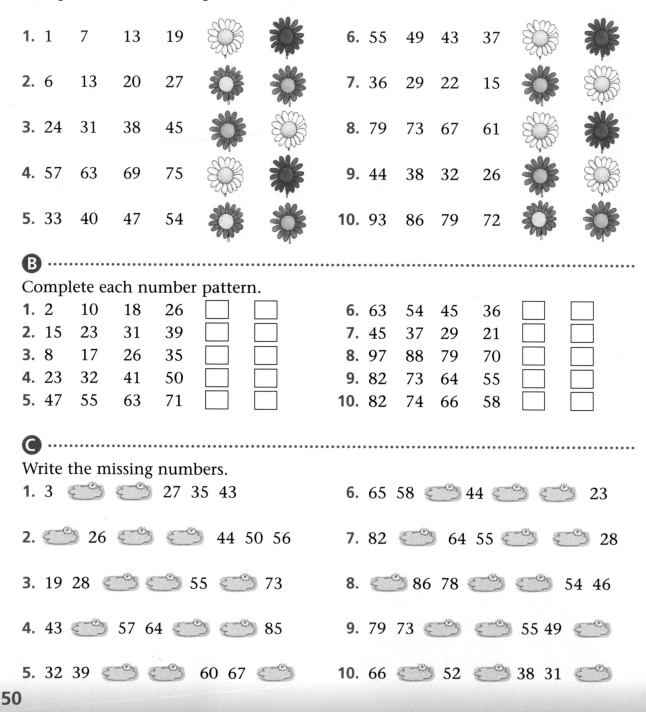

A

Complete each number pattern.

1. 1   7   13   19

2. 6   13   20   27

3. 24   31   38   45

4. 57   63   69   75

5. 33   40   47   54

6. 55   49   43   37

7. 36   29   22   15

8. 79   73   67   61

9. 44   38   32   26

10. 93   86   79   72

B

Complete each number pattern.

1. 2   10   18   26

2. 15   23   31   39

3. 8   17   26   35

4. 23   32   41   50

5. 47   55   63   71

6. 63   54   45   36

7. 45   37   29   21

8. 97   88   79   70

9. 82   73   64   55

10. 82   74   66   58

C

Write the missing numbers.

1. 3   ___   ___   27   35   43

2. ___   26   ___   ___   44   50   56

3. 19   28   ___   ___   55   ___   73

4. 43   ___   57   64   ___   ___   85

5. 32   39   ___   ___   60   67   ___

6. 65   58   ___   44   ___   ___   23

7. 82   ___   64   55   ___   ___   28

8. ___   86   78   ___   ___   54   46

9. 79   73   ___   ___   55   49   ___

10. 66   ___   52   ___   38   31   ___

50

Number Sequences

D ....

Complete each number pattern.

1. 3 14 25 36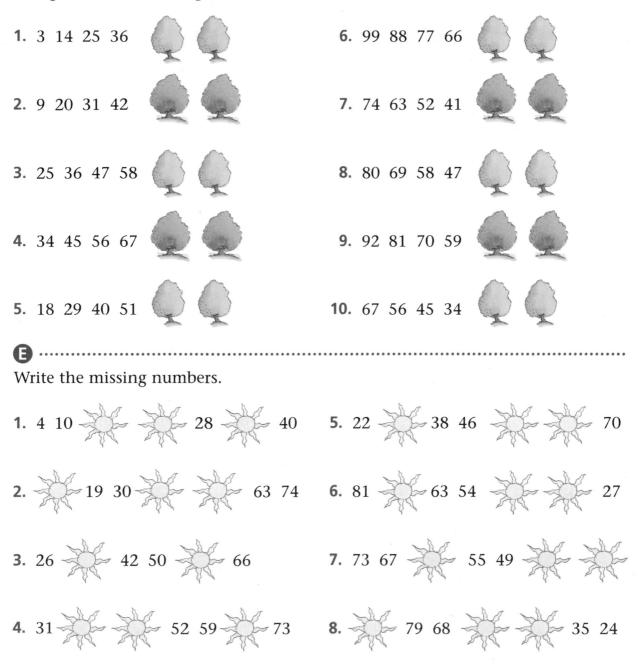

2. 9 20 31 42

3. 25 36 47 58

4. 34 45 56 67

5. 18 29 40 51

6. 99 88 77 66

7. 74 63 52 41

8. 80 69 58 47

9. 92 81 70 59

10. 67 56 45 34

E ....

Write the missing numbers.

1. 4 10 ☼ ☼ 28 ☼ 40

2. ☼ 19 30 ☼ ☼ 63 74

3. 26 ☼ 42 50 ☼ 66

4. 31 ☼ ☼ 52 59 ☼ 73

5. 22 ☼ 38 46 ☼ ☼ 70

6. 81 ☼ 63 54 ☼ ☼ 27

7. 73 67 ☼ 55 49 ☼ ☼

8. ☼ 79 68 ☼ ☼ 35 24

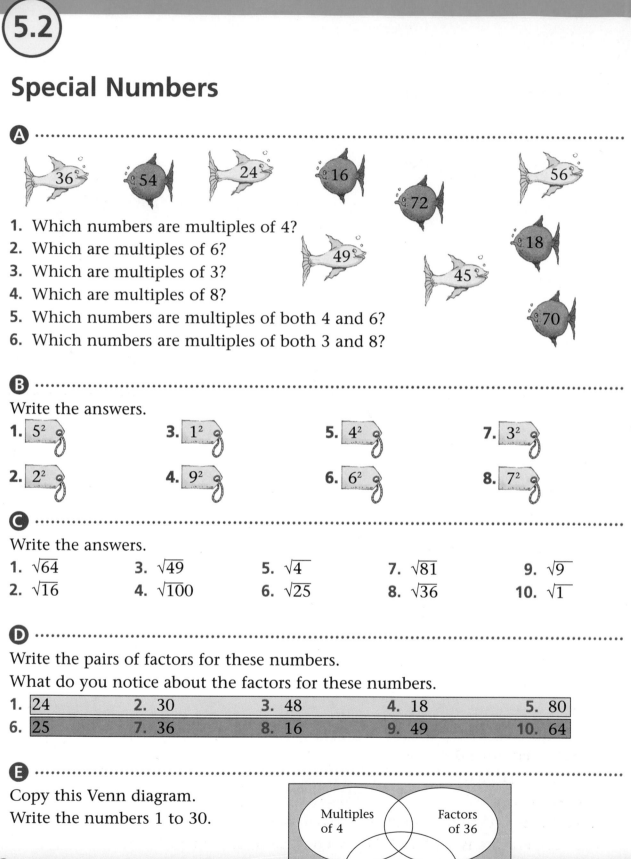

5.2

Special Numbers

A

36 54 24 16 56 72 18 49 45 70

1. Which numbers are multiples of 4?
2. Which are multiples of 6?
3. Which are multiples of 3?
4. Which are multiples of 8?
5. Which numbers are multiples of both 4 and 6?
6. Which numbers are multiples of both 3 and 8?

B

Write the answers.

1. 5^2
2. 2^2
3. 1^2
4. 9^2
5. 4^2
6. 6^2
7. 3^2
8. 7^2

C

Write the answers.

1. $\sqrt{64}$
2. $\sqrt{16}$
3. $\sqrt{49}$
4. $\sqrt{100}$
5. $\sqrt{4}$
6. $\sqrt{25}$
7. $\sqrt{81}$
8. $\sqrt{36}$
9. $\sqrt{9}$
10. $\sqrt{1}$

D

Write the pairs of factors for these numbers.
What do you notice about the factors for these numbers.

1. 24
2. 30
3. 48
4. 18
5. 80
6. 25
7. 36
8. 16
9. 49
10. 64

E

Copy this Venn diagram.
Write the numbers 1 to 30.

Multiples of 4   Factors of 36

Square numbers

52

5.3

Negative Numbers

A

Copy and complete each number pattern.

1. 6 4 2 0 ☐ ☐

2. 9 6 3 0 ☐ ☐

3. 5 3 1 ☐ 1 ☐ ☐

4. 7 4 1 ☐ ☐ ☐

5. ☐ 7 ☐ 5 ☐ 3 ☐ 1 ☐ ☐

6. ☐ 3 ☐ –1 ☐ –5 ☐ –9 ☐ ☐

7. 8 6 4 2 ☐ ☐ ☐ ☐ –8 ☐

8. 6 ☐ 4 3 2 ☐ ☐ –1 ☐ ☐

B

Write the number each arrow points to.

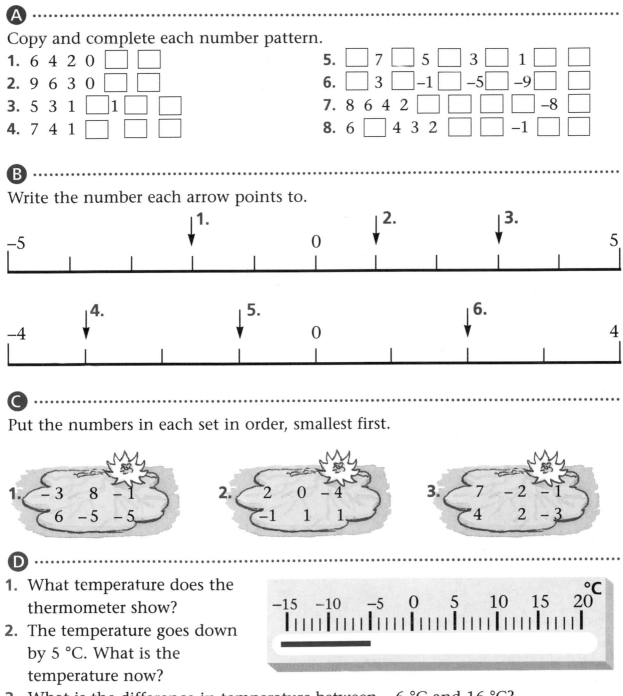

C

Put the numbers in each set in order, smallest first.

1. – 3 8 – 1 6 – 5 – 5

2. 2 0 – 4 –1 1 1

3. 7 – 2 – 1 4 2 – 3

D

1. What temperature does the thermometer show?
2. The temperature goes down by 5 °C. What is the temperature now?
3. What is the difference in temperature between –6 °C and 16 °C?
4. The temperature is –4 ° C. How much must it rise to reach 5 °C?

°C
–15 –10 –5 0 5 10 15 20

53

Negative Numbers

E

Write the difference in temperature between the pairs of thermometers.

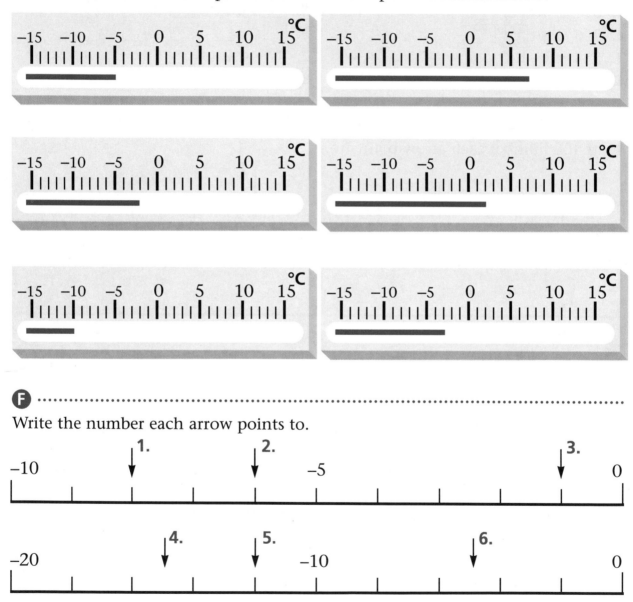

F

Write the number each arrow points to.

54

Summary for Unit 5

A

Copy and complete each pattern.

1. 35 41 47 ☐ ☐ ☐   3. 13 17 21 ☐ ☐ ☐   5. 25 33 41 ☐ ☐ ☐
2. 63 59 55 ☐ ☐ ☐   4. 81 79 77 ☐ ☐ ☐   6. 74 65 56 ☐ ☐ ☐

B

Write the missing numbers.

1. 34 36 ☐ ☐ ☐ 44   3. 9 ☐ 23 30 ☐ ☐   5. ☐ 21 30 ☐ ☐ 57
2. 48 ☐ ☐ 39 36 ☐   4. 92 ☐ ☐ ☐ 72 67   6. ☐ ☐ 58 ☐ 46 40

C

Write the answers.

1. 4^2 3. 3^2 5. 8^2 7. $\sqrt{4}$ 9. $\sqrt{81}$
2. 7^2 4. 10^2 6. $\sqrt{25}$ 8. $\sqrt{36}$ 10. $\sqrt{16}$

D

Copy these Venn diagrams.
Write the numbers 1 to 30 in each diagram.

E

Put the numbers in each set in order, starting with the smallest.

1. 4 −1 −6 1 0

2. 0 −2 1 3 −3

3. −5 −3 0 1 2

4. −8 7 −9 8 10

5. −7 7 8 −8 −6

6. −5 −2 3 0 4

55

Multiplication

Knowledge needed
✓ quick recall of multiplication facts
✓ knowledge of place value

Helpful facts

Multiplying decade numbers
Multiply significant numbers first then adjust for the tens:
multiply first
↓ ↓
$70 \times 80 = 5600$

Multiplying TU numbers by a single digit
Either
multiply tens first then units:
58×6
$(50 \times 6) + (8 \times 6)$
$300 + 48 = 348$
or
multiply units first then tens:
$(8 \times 6) + (50 \times 6)$
$48 + 300 = 348$

Approximating answers
Estimate an approximate answer before working out the exact answer, then check that the answer is sensible:
38×63 is approximately 40×60, which is 2400.
The exact answer is 2394.

Multiplication and division are opposites
Division is the opposite of multiplication.
This can be used to work out missing number problems:
$8 \times ? = 312$
$312 \div 8 = 39$

Pencil and paper methods
When a multiplication is too difficult to calculate mentally, use a written method:

```
    3 7
  x 4 9
  3 3 3
1 4 8 0
1 8 1 3
```

Where calculations are set out in columns, units should line up under units, tens under tens, etc.

Area method

When a multiplication is too difficult to calculate mentally, the area method can be used:

68 x 73

	70	3
60	4200	180
8	560	24

```
  4 3 8 0
+   5 8 4
  4 9 6 4
```

Halving and doubling

For some calculations, halve the smaller number and double the other:

34 x 8

68 x 4

136 x 2 = 272

Learning outcomes for UNIT 6

✓ can multiply HTU numbers by a single digit

✓ can multiply decade numbers by decade numbers

✓ develops a written method for calculating HTU x U and TU x TU

✓ estimates approximate answers to calculations involving multiplication

✓ uses a mental method to multiply TU numbers by a single digit

✓ solves word problems involving multiplication

Multiplying TU by TU

Complete these sums and check your answers.

1. 30 × 90	**3.** 80 × 60	**5.** 40 × 70	**7.** 40 × 30	**9.** 20 × 80
2. 50 × 40	**4.** 60 × 30	**6.** 90 × 90	**8.** 70 × 60	**10.** 80 × 50

A

Copy and complete these tables.

1.

× 30	
46	
61	
59	
32	

2.

× 50	
28	
93	
72	
53	

3.

× 80	
17	
34	
85	
92	

B

Write the answers.

1. 29 × 34	**3.** 16 × 52	**5.** 79 × 22	**7.** 26 × 57	**9.** 85 × 56
2. 45 × 81	**4.** 63 × 94	**6.** 18 × 75	**8.** 38 × 99	**10.** 67 × 42

C

Calculate and write the area of these rectangles.

1. 36 cm, 73 cm

2. 68 cm, 85 cm

3. 24 cm, 92 cm

4. 17 cm, 49 cm

D

1. Theatre tickets cost £14. How much will 28 tickets cost?
2. A bag of crisps weighs 35 g. There are 46 bags in a box. How much will the box of crisps weigh in total?
3. Mr Wright travels 67 km every week. How far will he have travelled in one year?
4. There are 48 eggs on a tray. How many eggs will there be on 75 trays?

6.6

Mixed Multiplication

Complete these sums and check your answers.

1. 3×7 4. 5×8 7. 5×90 10. 400×9
2. 8×9 5. 80×4 8. 60×7 11. 700×8
3. 6×4 6. 20×7 9. 600×3 12. 7×500

A

Write the total weight of each of these.

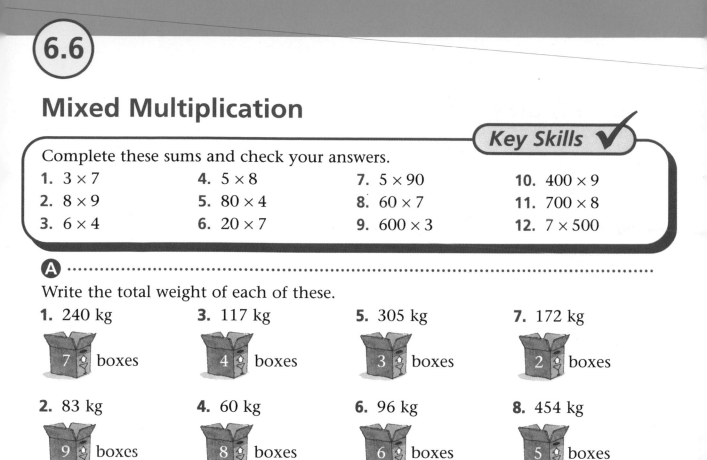

1. 240 kg
   7 ⬥ boxes

3. 117 kg
   4 ⬥ boxes

5. 305 kg
   3 ⬥ boxes

7. 172 kg
   2 ⬥ boxes

2. 83 kg
   9 ⬥ boxes

4. 60 kg
   8 ⬥ boxes

6. 96 kg
   6 ⬥ boxes

8. 454 kg
   5 ⬥ boxes

B

Write which sum in each pair gives the larger product.

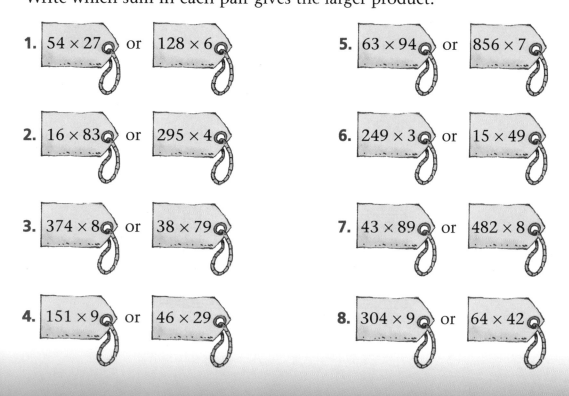

1. 54×27 or 128×6

2. 16×83 or 295×4

3. 374×8 or 38×79

4. 151×9 or 46×29

5. 63×94 or 856×7

6. 249×3 or 15×49

7. 43×89 or 482×8

8. 304×9 or 64×42

Mixed Multiplication

C ···

Write the product of each pair of numbers.

1. 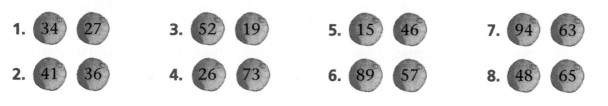 34 27

2. 41 36

3. 52 19

4. 26 73

5. 15 46

6. 89 57

7. 94 63

8. 48 65

D ···

This table shows how much foreign currency can be changed for £1.

Iceland	105 Kronas
Mexico	5 Pesos
Thailand	38 Baht
Japan	152 Yen
Pakistan	47 Rupees
Austria	16 Schillings

Write how many:

1. Pesos in £45?
2. Kronas in £9?
3. Yen in £8?

4. Rupees in £23?
5. Schillings in £39?
6. Baht in £52?

E ···

Copy and complete these tables.

1.

× 16	
32	
14	
60	
85	

2.

× 28	
54	
77	
12	
23	

3.

× 43	
96	
41	
65	
38	

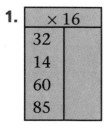

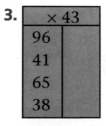

6.7

Multiplication Problems

Complete these sums and check your answers.

1. 6×9 4. 9×9 7. 60×6 10. 400×9
2. 4×7 5. 50×4 8. 7×80 11. 800×4
3. 8×5 6. 90×3 9. 5×300 12. 6×700

A

Write the answers.

1. Each person in Meerha's class brought 8 leaves to school. There are 27 children in the class. How many leaves did they have in total?
2. A train holds 49 passengers. How many passengers will there be on 5 trains?

3. Ali gets £3 a week pocket money.
   How much pocket money does he get in a year?
4. Christmas cards are sold in packs of 8. Three children each buy 6 packs of cards. How many cards do the three children have altogether?

B

Write the total amounts.

1. 330 ml
   6 cans

2. 454 g
   8 boxes

3. 500 g
   4 bags

4. 156 ml
   9 keys

5. 387 g
   5 boxes

6. 523 ml
   3 bowls

7. 267 g
   7 purses

8. 9 kg
   145 wheels

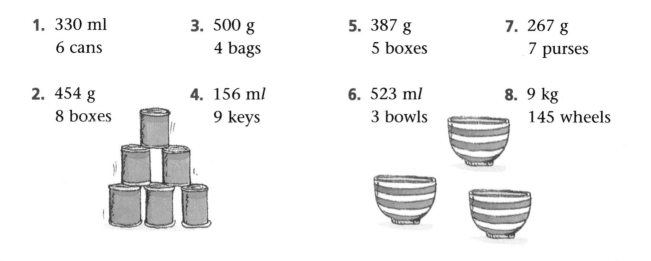

Multiplication Problems

C ....

Write the totals on this order form.

Item	Cost per item	Number of items	Total cost
Football	£23	14	
Tennis racquet	£47	36	
Hockey stick	£35	38	
Basketball	£19	27	
Floor mats	£78	25	
Netball	£24	19	

D ....

Write the answers.

1. A lorry travels 368 km a day.
   How many kilometres will it have travelled after 5 days?
2. What number is 8 times greater than 74?
3. Multiply 59 by 87.
4. Kim measures her garden with a stick. The stick is 63 cm long and her garden is 49 sticks long. How long is Kim's garden in centimetres?

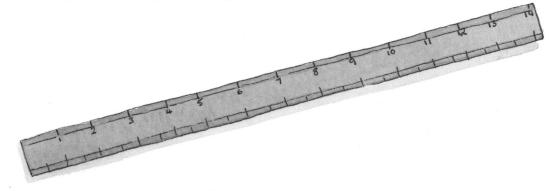

Summary for Unit 6

A

Copy and complete the tables.

→ In | × 4 | Out →

IN	40	60	500	300	92
OUT					

→ In | × 7 | Out →

IN	30	20	800	500	74
OUT					

B

Write the answers.

1. 341×2 **3.** 502×4 **5.** 483×3 **7.** 714×7

2. 263×5 **4.** 627×6 **6.** 197×8 **8.** 835×9

C

Copy and complete the multiplication tables.

1.

×	30	60	80
70			
600			
700			

2.

×	400	90	500
20			
80			
30			

D

Write the product of each pair of numbers.

1. 45 70   **3.** 24 53   **5.** 61 38   **7.** 19 82

2. 96 35   **4.** 67 88   **6.** 59 54   **8.** 93 37

E

1. There are 52 cards in a pack. How many cards will there be in 5 packs?
2. What is double 482?
3. Multiply 70 by 9.
4. A bag of flour weighs 450 g. How much will 3 bags weigh?
5. What number is 6 times greater than 236?
6. A floor tile measures 60 cm by 70 cm. What is the area of the floor tile?

Knowledge needed

- ✓ quick recall of multiplication facts
- ✓ multiplication and division are inverses
- ✓ quick recall of division facts

Helpful facts

Dividing by 2: halving
Dividing by 2 is the same as halving:

$72 \div 2 = 36$

half of $72 = 36$

Halving odd numbers gives an answer with a half in it:

half of $85 = 42\frac{1}{2}$ half of $97 = 48\frac{1}{2}$

Remainders
These are the remainders possible when dividing by:

6   0, 1, 2, 3, 4, 5
7   0, 1, 2, 3, 4, 5, 6
8   0, 1, 2, 3, 4, 5, 6, 7
9   0, 1, 2, 3, 4, 5, 6, 7, 8,
10   0, 1, 2, 3, 4, 5, 6, 7, 8, 9

Rules of divisibility
Whole numbers are divisible by:

10	if the last digit is 0	350, 2900, 6730, 2190 ....
5	if the last digit is 0 or 5	455, 260, 385, 205 ......
2	if the last digit is an even number	244, 8776, 3108, 2330 ....
3	if the sum of the digits is divisible by 3	81, 162, 255, 834 ......
4	if the last two digits are divisible by 4	144, 1328, 3640, 2076 .....
6	if it is even and also divisible by 3	126, 384, 1056, 3348 ....
8	if half of it is divisible by 4	144, 576, 440, 984 .....
9	if the sum of the digits is divisible by 9	324, 2052, 5787, 2907 .....

Approximating answers

Estimate an approximate answer before working out the exact answer, then check that the answer is sensible: $612 \div 3$ is approximately $600 \div 3$, which is 200.
The exact answer is 204.

Multiplication and division are opposites

Division is the opposite of multiplication.
This can be used to work out missing number problems:
$? \div 6 = 42$
$42 \times 6 = 252$

Pencil and paper methods

When a division is too difficult to calculate mentally, use a written method.
This method is developed from repeated subtraction:

```
        2 3
   6) 1 3 8
    _ 1 2 0    (6 x 20)
        1 8
    _   1 8    (6 x 3)
          0
```

Learning outcomes for UNIT 7

✓ knows rules of divisibility for ÷2 to ÷10
✓ uses a mental method to divide TU numbers by a single digit, with and without remainders
✓ can divide HTU numbers by a single digit, with and without remainders
✓ knows when to round up and round down remainders
✓ estimates approximate answers to calculations involving division
✓ develops a written method for calculating HTU ÷ U and TU ÷ U
✓ solves word problems involving division

Dividing TU by U

Key Skills ✔

Complete these sums and check your answers.
1. 9 ÷ 3   **3.** 6 ÷ 3   **5.** 8 ÷ 4   **7.** 8 ÷ 2   **9.** 7 ÷ 1
2. 4 ÷ 4   **4.** 10 ÷ 5   **6.** 12 ÷ 6   **8.** 5 ÷ 5   **10.** 12 ÷ 6

A

Copy and write the missing numbers.

1. ☐ ÷ 7
     5
   ☐ ÷ 8   ☐ ÷ 5

4. ☐ ÷ 5
     4
   ☐ ÷ 7   ☐ ÷ 9

7. ☐ ÷ 5
     9
   ☐ ÷ 7   ☐ ÷ 9

2. ☐ ÷ 3
     8
   ☐ ÷ 9   ☐ ÷ 4

5. ☐ ÷ 4
     6
   ☐ ÷ 3   ☐ ÷ 8

8. ☐ ÷ 8
     7
   ☐ ÷ 6   ☐ ÷ 2

3. ☐ ÷ 2
     6
   ☐ ÷ 7   ☐ ÷ 9

6. ☐ ÷ 7
     10
   ☐ ÷ 3   ☐ ÷ 6

9. ☐ ÷ 3
     9
   ☐ ÷ 4   ☐ ÷ 6

B

Write the answer and remainder.

1. 39 ÷ 6	**5.** 23 ÷ 3	**9.** 26 ÷ 4	**13.** 26 ÷ 5	**17.** 31 ÷ 9
2. 42 ÷ 5	**6.** 51 ÷ 8	**10.** 38 ÷ 4	**14.** 19 ÷ 2	**18.** 14 ÷ 3
3. 15 ÷ 7	**7.** 67 ÷ 9	**11.** 58 ÷ 7	**15.** 20 ÷ 6	**19.** 33 ÷ 8
4. 28 ÷ 6	**8.** 52 ÷ 5	**12.** 16 ÷ 3	**16.** 68 ÷ 9	**20.** 55 ÷ 6

Dividing TU by U

C ....

Write the answers.

1. $3\overline{)81}$ 5. $5\overline{)80}$ 9. $8\overline{)96}$ 13. $9\overline{)126}$ 17. $4\overline{)112}$

2. $4\overline{)72}$ 6. $7\overline{)98}$ 10. $6\overline{)78}$ 14. $6\overline{)144}$ 18. $5\overline{)300}$

3. $4\overline{)99}$ 7. $7\overline{)69}$ 11. $3\overline{)82}$ 15. $9\overline{)196}$ 19. $7\overline{)101}$

4. $5\overline{)86}$ 8. $4\overline{)51}$ 12. $7\overline{)200}$ 16. $6\overline{)205}$ 20. $3\overline{)199}$

D ....

Copy and write the missing digits.

1.   remainder **3**

   6 ☐ ÷ 4   5 ☐ ÷ 3
   7 ☐ ÷ 5   9 ☐ ÷ 8

3.   remainder **2**

   8 ☐ ÷ 6   8 ☐ ÷ 7
   6 ☐ ÷ 5   9 ☐ ÷ 6

2.   remainder **4**

   2 ☐ ÷ 6   2 ☐ ÷ 4
   3 ☐ ÷ 5   4 ☐ ÷ 9

4.   remainder **5**

   7 ☐ ÷ 9   12 ☐ ÷ 12
   7 ☐ ÷ 8   11 ☐ ÷ 11

E ....

Copy and complete.

1. →In ÷6 Out→

Factors of 6

In	6		18		30
Out		2		4	

2. →In ÷7 Out→

Factors of 7

In		14		35	
Out	1		3		6

3. →In ÷8 Out→

Factors of 8

In	8		24		40	48	
Out		2		4			7

7.2

Dividing HTU by U (No Remainders)

A

Copy and complete these.

1. 6⟌366   4. 8⟌584   7. 9⟌513   10. 7⟌602
2. 5⟌700   5. 4⟌872   8. 7⟌336   11. 4⟌924
3. 3⟌618   6. 6⟌900   9. 5⟌485   12. 6⟌792

B

Divide each number by 3	Divide each number by 7	Divide each number by 8
252	231	216
813	476	992
495	763	744
297	532	520

C

Copy and write the missing digit.

1. 4⟌□36 (34)   3. 5⟌4□5 (95)   5. 6⟌25□ (43)   7. 9⟌□04 (56)

2. 6⟌474 (7□)   4. 9⟌468 (□2)   6. 9⟌144 (1□)   8. 7⟌5□8 (84)

D

Ben has the following plants:

Roses   248
Daffodils   432
Lavender   360
Tulips   768
Primulas   512

1. Equal numbers of each plant are put into 4 tubs. How many of each plant will be in one tub?

2. Equal numbers of each plant are put into 8 tubs. How many of each plant will be in one tub?

7.3

Dividing HTU by U

Complete these sums and check your answers.
1. $160 \div 4$ 3. $400 \div 5$ 5. $560 \div 7$ 7. $640 \div 8$ 9. $280 \div 7$
2. $360 \div 9$ 4. $420 \div 6$ 6. $270 \div 3$ 8. $630 \div 9$ 10. $200 \div 5$

A ....

Copy and complete these.
1. $6\overline{)425}$ 4. $9\overline{)738}$ 7. $8\overline{)354}$ 10. $6\overline{)885}$
2. $2\overline{)419}$ 5. $4\overline{)962}$ 8. $3\overline{)141}$ 11. $7\overline{)996}$
3. $5\overline{)603}$ 6. $7\overline{)500}$ 9. $5\overline{)287}$ 12. $8\overline{)293}$

B ....

Write the sums which have a remainder of 3.

$246 \div 3$ $305 \div 4$ $114 \div 6$ $748 \div 5$ $473 \div 6$

$129 \div 7$ $187 \div 8$ $523 \div 9$ $732 \div 9$ $691 \div 7$

C ....

Copy and write the missing digit.

1. $4\overline{)\square54}$ — 88r2   3. $3\overline{)14\square}$ — 47r1   5. $5\overline{)1\square4}$ — 62r4   7. $6\overline{)4\square9}$ — 73r1   9. $5\overline{)\square72}$ — 54r2

2. $7\overline{)276}$ — 39r$\square$ 4. $8\overline{)734}$ — $\square$1r6   6. $9\overline{)235}$ — 2$\square$r1   8. $7\overline{)137}$ — 19r$\square$ 10. $9\overline{)610}$ — $\square$7r7

D ....

Write the answers.

259   342   269   680   255

1. Which of these numbers can be divided exactly by 6?
2. Which of these numbers has a remainder of 3 when divided by 9?
3. Which of these numbers can be divided exactly by 4?
4. Which of these numbers has a remainder of 4 when divided by 5?
5. Which of these numbers has an answer of 37 when divided by 7?

7.4

Dividing by Multiples of 10

Divide each of these by 10.
1. 70   **3.** 80   **5.** 100   **7.** 260   **9.** 730
2. 50   **4.** 20   **6.** 140   **8.** 400   **10.** 590

A ....

Write the answers.
1. 240 ÷ 20   **3.** 180 ÷ 30   **5.** 320 ÷ 40   **7.** 150 ÷ 50   **9.** 160 ÷ 20
2. 280 ÷ 40   **4.** 400 ÷ 50   **6.** 270 ÷ 30   **8.** 200 ÷ 40   **10.** 120 ÷ 30

B ....

Look at the number machines. Copy and complete the tables.

→ In | ÷60 | Out →

IN	480	360	600	240
OUT				

→ In | ÷70 | Out →

IN	210	420	700	490
OUT				

→ In | ÷90 | Out →

IN	360	540	180	630
OUT				

→ In | ÷80 | Out →

IN	720	240	560	320
OUT				

C ....

Write the answers.

280   630   450   540   810

1. Which of these numbers can be divided exactly by 40?
2. Which of these numbers can be divided exactly by 50?
3. Which of these numbers can be divided exactly by 60?
4. Which of these numbers cannot be divided exactly by 90?

Division Problems

A ....

Write the answers.

1. There are 93 children. They are put into 3 equal–size classes.
   How many children are there in each class?
2. Mrs Adams buys each of her 8 grandchildren a skateboard for Christmas.
   Altogether she spent £96. What is the price of one skateboard?
3. A machine puts 5 crayons into one packet.
   How many packets can 90 crayons fill?
4. How many weeks are there in September, October and November?
5. 4 children share 92 badges equally between them.
   How many badges do they each get?

B ....

This table shows the number of eggs collected each day at a farm. The eggs are
put into cartons that hold 6 eggs. Copy and complete the table.

	No. of eggs collected	No. of full cartons	No. of eggs left over
Mon	86	14	
Tues	75		
Weds	93		
Thurs	79		
Fri	82		

C ....

What is the weight or volume of one single item in each multipack?

| 8 packets of crisps total weight 224 g | 9 packs of tissues total weight 243 g | 6 chocolate bars total weight 444 g |

| 4 cans of drink total volume 992 ml | 3 packs of biscuits total weight 591 g | 2 cans of beans total weight 838 g |

Division Problems

D ....

A piece of ribbon is 839 cm long.
What is the length of the piece of ribbon that is left over
when the ribbon is cut into:

1. 4 equal pieces   **3.** 2 equal pieces   **5.** 6 equal pieces   **7.** 5 equal pieces
2. 7 equal pieces   **4.** 8 equal pieces   **6.** 3 equal pieces   **8.** 9 equal pieces

E ....

Write the answers.

1. 858 ml of water is shared equally between three glasses.
   How much water will there be in one glass?
2. There are four full weeks in July and how many days?
3. 384 photos are put into an album. Each page has 9 photos.
   The last page will not be full, how many photos will there be on this page?
4. 4 train tickets cost £92. What is the cost of one ticket?

5. Fred buys 6 theatre tickets for £96. How much was the cost of each ticket?
6. Shirin's car had 4 new tyres and the bill came to £132.
   How much did 1 tyre cost?

7. Emil went to see a football match with Cara.
   They spent 94p on two cans of cola. How much did one can cost?
8. 9 identical letters weighed a total of 738 g. What's the weight of one letter?

76

Summary for Unit 7

A

Write the answer and the remainder.

1. 45 ÷ 7   **3.** 33 ÷ 4   **5.** 17 ÷ 8   **7.** 26 ÷ 5   **9.** 51 ÷ 6

2. 25 ÷ 3   **4.** 41 ÷ 9   **6.** 57 ÷ 8   **8.** 27 ÷ 6   **10.** 39 ÷ 7

B

Copy and complete the table.

Divide each number by 4	Divide each number by 9	Divide each number by 6
152	207	288
388	414	114
292	567	522
260	306	546

C

1. What is left over when 234 is shared equally by 4?
2. Find the remainder of 640 divided by 7.
3. A bottle holds 128 ml of medicine. One 5 ml spoonful is taken each day.
   How many days will the medicine last?
4. A train breaks down and 8 buses come to collect the 387 passengers.
   All the buses hold the same number of passengers.
   How many passengers remain without a bus?

D

Copy and complete the tables.

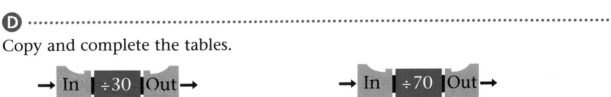

IN	180	270		
OUT			8	7

IN	210	490		
OUT			5	9

Knowledge needed

✓ simple division facts

Helpful facts

> < = symbols

> means is larger than

< means is smaller than

= means is equal to

$$\frac{1}{3} > \frac{1}{4} \qquad \frac{1}{2} < \frac{3}{4} \qquad \frac{1}{2} = \frac{4}{8}$$

Equivalent fractions

Some fractions are worth the same even though they may look different:

$$\frac{1}{2} = \frac{2}{4} = \frac{3}{6} = \frac{4}{8}$$

$$\frac{2}{3} = \frac{4}{6} = \frac{6}{9} = \frac{8}{12}$$

$$\frac{3}{4} = \frac{6}{8} = \frac{9}{12} = \frac{12}{16}$$

$$\frac{3}{5} = \frac{6}{10} = \frac{9}{15} = \frac{12}{20}$$

Equivalent strips

Equivalent strips help to compare fractions which are the same:

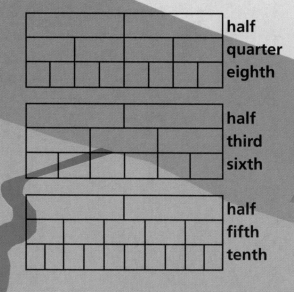

half
quarter
eighth

half
third
sixth

half
fifth
tenth

Mixed numbers

These are whole numbers and fractions: $1\frac{3}{4}$, $2\frac{1}{3}$, $4\frac{7}{8}$

Mixed numbers can be changed to top heavy fractions (or improper):

$$1\frac{2}{3} = \frac{5}{3} \qquad 2\frac{3}{4} = \frac{11}{4}$$

Fractions of quantities

$\frac{1}{2}$ is the same as ÷ 2 $\frac{1}{2}$ of 14 = 7

$\frac{1}{5}$ is the same as ÷ 5 $\frac{1}{5}$ of 65 = 13

$\frac{1}{10}$ is the same as ÷ 10 $\frac{1}{10}$ of 120 = 12

$\frac{1}{3}$ is the same as ÷ 3 $\frac{1}{3}$ of 21 = 7

$\frac{1}{4}$ is the same as ÷ 4 $\frac{1}{4}$ of 44 = 11

Rounding

If the fraction is less than $\frac{1}{2}$, round down:

$4\frac{1}{8}$ metre is approximately 4 metres

If the fraction is $\frac{1}{2}$ or more, round up:

$1\frac{3}{4}$ kg is approximately 2 kg

Denominators and numerators

The denominator shows how
many parts the fraction is divided into.
The numerator shows how many parts are taken.

$$\frac{2 \leftarrow \text{numerator}}{3 \leftarrow \text{denominator}}$$

Comparing and ordering fractions

When comparing two fractions for size, make the
denominators the same and compare the numerators.
Which is larger, $\frac{3}{4}$ or $\frac{5}{8}$?

Make them both eighths: $\frac{3}{4} = \frac{6}{8}$ so $\frac{6}{8} > \frac{5}{8}$ and $\frac{3}{4} > \frac{5}{8}$

Learning outcomes for UNIT 8

✓ recognises and uses unitary and non-unitary fractions
✓ finds fractions of quantities
✓ knows equivalence of fractions
✓ compares and orders fractions
✓ changes improper fractions to mixed numbers and mixed
   numbers to improper fractions
✓ rounds fractions to the nearest whole unit

Fractions of Quantities

A ....

Find a quarter of each of these.

1. 28p	**4.** 32 kg	**7.** 60p	**10.** 56 mm
2. 64 g	**5.** 76 km	**8.** 96 g	**11.** £44
3. 92 m*l*	**6.** 88p	**9.** 100 m*l*	**12.** 36 cm

B ....

Write the answers.

1. $\frac{1}{3}$ of 21   **4.** $\frac{1}{5}$ of 75   **7.** $\frac{1}{6}$ of 54   **10.** $\frac{1}{3}$ of 72

2. $\frac{1}{8}$ of 16   **5.** $\frac{1}{2}$ of 90   **8.** $\frac{1}{9}$ of 27   **11.** $\frac{1}{2}$ of 160

3. $\frac{1}{10}$ of 200   **6.** $\frac{1}{7}$ of 56   **9.** $\frac{1}{10}$ of 130   **12.** $\frac{1}{6}$ of 96

C ....

Two-thirds is cut from each piece of ribbon. Write how much is cut from each length. What is left?

1. 9 cm   **5.** 12 cm   **9.** 60 cm

2. 15 cm   **6.** 30 cm   **10.** 48 cm

3. 27 cm   **7.** 18 cm   **11.** 69 cm

4. 21 cm   **8.** 36 cm   **12.** 75 cm

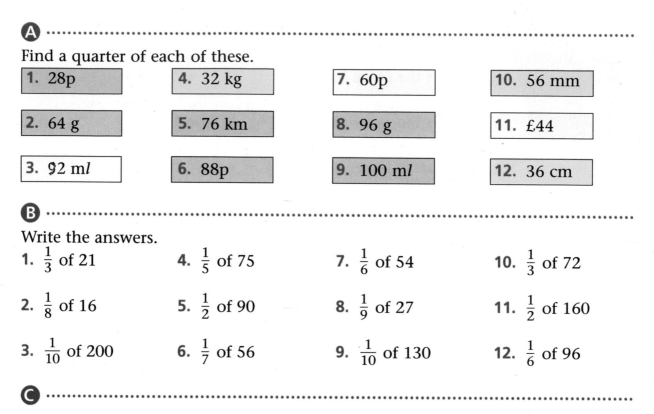
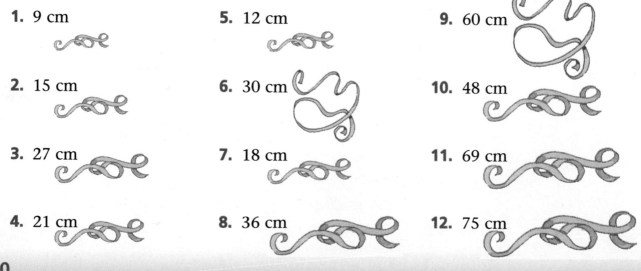

Fractions of Quantities

D ....

Find $\frac{3}{4}$ of each of these.

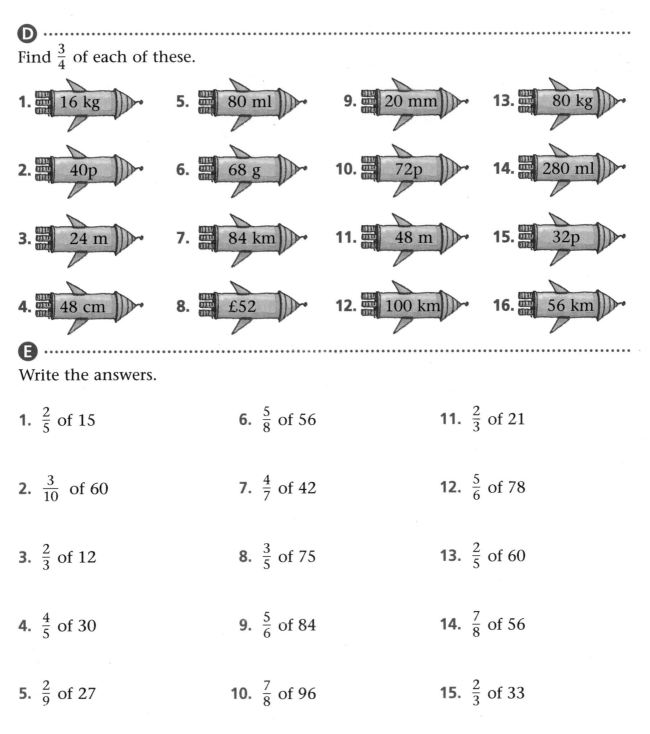

1. 16 kg

2. 40p

3. 24 m

4. 48 cm

5. 80 ml

6. 68 g

7. 84 km

8. £52

9. 20 mm

10. 72p

11. 48 m

12. 100 km

13. 80 kg

14. 280 ml

15. 32p

16. 56 km

E ....

Write the answers.

1. $\frac{2}{5}$ of 15

2. $\frac{3}{10}$ of 60

3. $\frac{2}{3}$ of 12

4. $\frac{4}{5}$ of 30

5. $\frac{2}{9}$ of 27

6. $\frac{5}{8}$ of 56

7. $\frac{4}{7}$ of 42

8. $\frac{3}{5}$ of 75

9. $\frac{5}{6}$ of 84

10. $\frac{7}{8}$ of 96

11. $\frac{2}{3}$ of 21

12. $\frac{5}{6}$ of 78

13. $\frac{2}{5}$ of 60

14. $\frac{7}{8}$ of 56

15. $\frac{2}{3}$ of 33

8.2

Equivalent Fractions

A

Copy and complete these equivalent fractions.

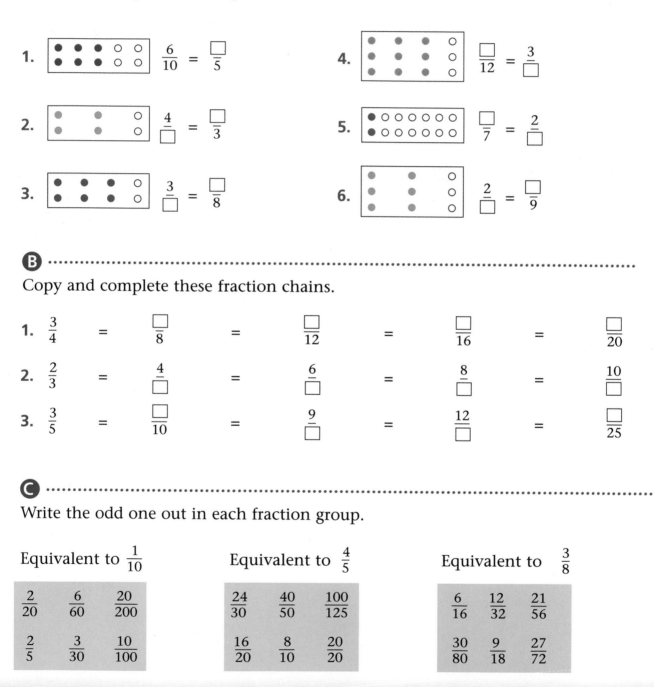

1. $\dfrac{6}{10} = \dfrac{\square}{5}$

2. $\dfrac{4}{\square} = \dfrac{\square}{3}$

3. $\dfrac{3}{\square} = \dfrac{\square}{8}$

4. $\dfrac{\square}{12} = \dfrac{3}{\square}$

5. $\dfrac{\square}{7} = \dfrac{2}{\square}$

6. $\dfrac{2}{\square} = \dfrac{\square}{9}$

B

Copy and complete these fraction chains.

1. $\dfrac{3}{4} = \dfrac{\square}{8} = \dfrac{\square}{12} = \dfrac{\square}{16} = \dfrac{\square}{20}$

2. $\dfrac{2}{3} = \dfrac{4}{\square} = \dfrac{6}{\square} = \dfrac{8}{\square} = \dfrac{10}{\square}$

3. $\dfrac{3}{5} = \dfrac{\square}{10} = \dfrac{9}{\square} = \dfrac{12}{\square} = \dfrac{\square}{25}$

C

Write the odd one out in each fraction group.

Equivalent to $\dfrac{1}{10}$

$\dfrac{2}{20}$	$\dfrac{6}{60}$	$\dfrac{20}{200}$
$\dfrac{2}{5}$	$\dfrac{3}{30}$	$\dfrac{10}{100}$

Equivalent to $\dfrac{4}{5}$

$\dfrac{24}{30}$	$\dfrac{40}{50}$	$\dfrac{100}{125}$
$\dfrac{16}{20}$	$\dfrac{8}{10}$	$\dfrac{20}{20}$

Equivalent to $\dfrac{3}{8}$

$\dfrac{6}{16}$	$\dfrac{12}{32}$	$\dfrac{21}{56}$
$\dfrac{30}{80}$	$\dfrac{9}{18}$	$\dfrac{27}{72}$

Comparing and Ordering Fractions

A

Write which fraction is the smaller in each of these pairs.

1. $\frac{3}{5}$ or $\frac{7}{10}$ 3. $\frac{1}{2}$ or $\frac{1}{4}$ 5. $\frac{1}{2}$ or $\frac{3}{8}$ 7. $\frac{2}{3}$ or $\frac{11}{12}$

2. $\frac{2}{3}$ or $\frac{5}{6}$ 4. $\frac{3}{4}$ or $\frac{5}{8}$ 6. $\frac{3}{4}$ or $\frac{3}{16}$ 8. $\frac{1}{5}$ or $\frac{1}{20}$

B

Write which fraction is the larger in each of these pairs.

1. $\frac{2}{3}$ or $\frac{7}{5}$ 3. $\frac{3}{4}$ or $\frac{11}{12}$ 5. $\frac{4}{5}$ or $\frac{13}{20}$ 7. $\frac{2}{5}$ or $\frac{7}{15}$

2. $\frac{1}{2}$ or $\frac{7}{12}$ 4. $\frac{1}{3}$ or $\frac{1}{9}$ 6. $\frac{1}{4}$ or $\frac{3}{20}$ 8. $\frac{1}{5}$ or $\frac{2}{15}$

C

Write each set of fractions in order, starting with the smallest.

1. $\frac{1}{3}$ $\frac{1}{5}$ $\frac{1}{2}$ $\frac{1}{4}$ 4. $\frac{1}{10}$ $\frac{2}{5}$ $\frac{3}{5}$ $\frac{7}{10}$

2. $\frac{1}{10}$ $\frac{1}{7}$ $\frac{1}{12}$ $\frac{1}{15}$ 5. $\frac{3}{4}$ $\frac{5}{8}$ $\frac{1}{4}$ $\frac{7}{8}$

3. $\frac{1}{6}$ $\frac{1}{4}$ $\frac{1}{20}$ $\frac{1}{15}$ 6. $\frac{1}{2}$ $\frac{3}{4}$ $\frac{5}{12}$ $\frac{1}{12}$

D

Copy these, putting < > or = to make each statement true.

1. $\frac{1}{5}$ 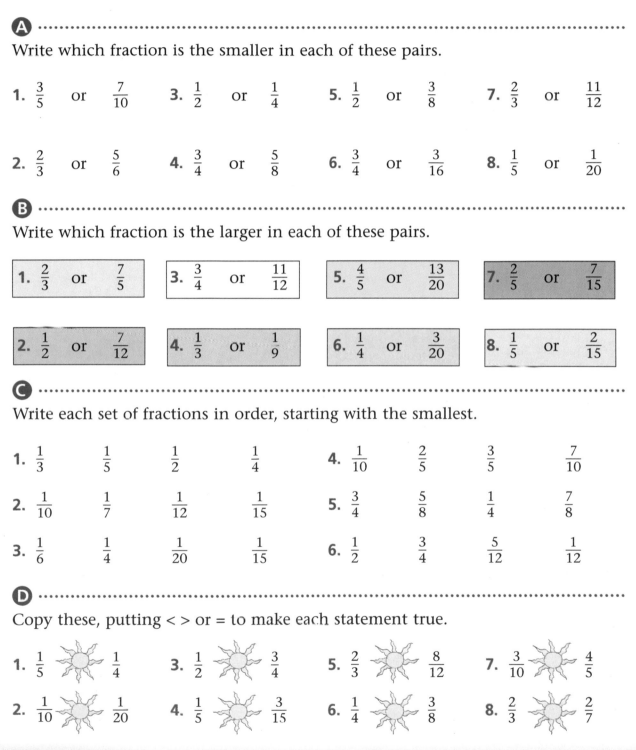 $\frac{1}{4}$ 3. $\frac{1}{2}$ ✶ $\frac{3}{4}$ 5. $\frac{2}{3}$ ✶ $\frac{8}{12}$ 7. $\frac{3}{10}$ ✶ $\frac{4}{5}$

2. $\frac{1}{10}$ ✶ $\frac{1}{20}$ 4. $\frac{1}{5}$ ✶ $\frac{3}{15}$ 6. $\frac{1}{4}$ ✶ $\frac{3}{8}$ 8. $\frac{2}{3}$ ✶ $\frac{2}{7}$

Improper Fractions and Mixed Numbers

A

Change these whole numbers into fractions.

	halves			tenths			thirds
1.	3		5.	1		9.	2
2.	5		6.	4		10.	5
3.	6		7.	3		11.	10
4.	7		8.	7		12.	8

B

Write these as improper fractions.

1. $4\frac{1}{2}$ 4. $5\frac{2}{5}$ 7. $4\frac{2}{3}$ 10. $5\frac{3}{10}$

2. $6\frac{1}{3}$ 5. $2\frac{1}{4}$ 8. $2\frac{5}{6}$ 11. $3\frac{6}{7}$

3. $1\frac{3}{4}$ 6. $3\frac{1}{6}$ 9. $1\frac{4}{5}$ 12. $6\frac{3}{8}$

C

Write these as mixed numbers.

1. $\frac{4}{2}$ 4. $\frac{3}{2}$ 7. $\frac{10}{3}$ 10. $\frac{22}{7}$

2. $\frac{5}{3}$ 5. $\frac{5}{5}$ 8. $\frac{7}{5}$ 11. $\frac{13}{9}$

3. $\frac{7}{4}$ 6. $\frac{12}{4}$ 9. $\frac{19}{8}$ 12. $\frac{17}{6}$

D

Copy and complete the equivalent fractions.

1. $\frac{\square}{2} = 3\frac{1}{2}$ 4. $\frac{9}{2} = 4\frac{\square}{2}$ 7. $\frac{\square}{5} = 3\frac{1}{5}$

2. $\frac{5}{\square} = 1\frac{1}{4}$ 5. $\frac{12}{5} = 2\frac{2}{\square}$ 8. $\frac{23}{4} = \square\frac{3}{4}$

3. $\frac{5}{3} = \square\frac{2}{3}$ 6. $\frac{14}{\square} = 4\frac{2}{3}$ 9. $\frac{23}{6} = 3\frac{\square}{6}$

8.5

Fractions and Measures

A

Write the answers.

1. $2\frac{1}{2}$ m = 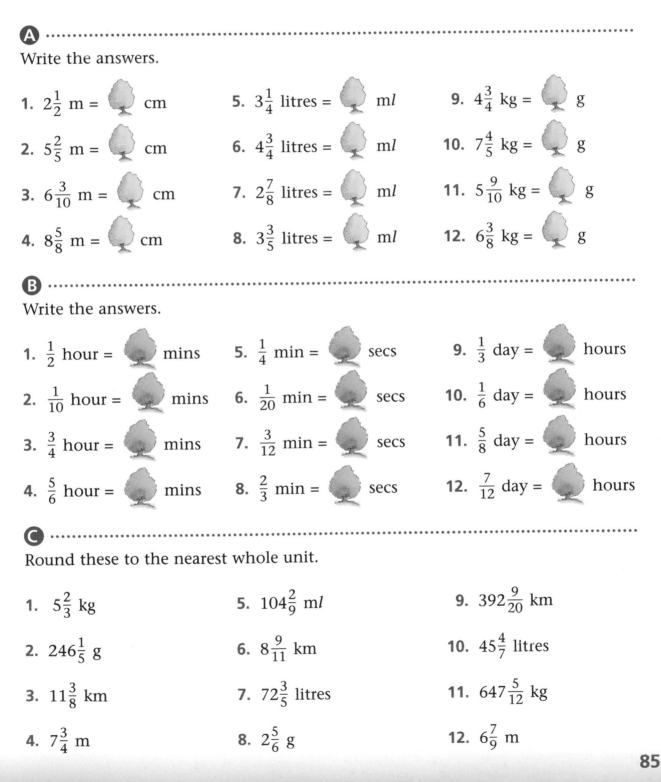 cm

2. $5\frac{2}{5}$ m = cm

3. $6\frac{3}{10}$ m = cm

4. $8\frac{5}{8}$ m = cm

5. $3\frac{1}{4}$ litres = ml

6. $4\frac{3}{4}$ litres = ml

7. $2\frac{7}{8}$ litres = ml

8. $3\frac{3}{5}$ litres = ml

9. $4\frac{3}{4}$ kg = g

10. $7\frac{4}{5}$ kg = g

11. $5\frac{9}{10}$ kg = g

12. $6\frac{3}{8}$ kg = g

B

Write the answers.

1. $\frac{1}{2}$ hour = mins

2. $\frac{1}{10}$ hour = mins

3. $\frac{3}{4}$ hour = mins

4. $\frac{5}{6}$ hour = mins

5. $\frac{1}{4}$ min = secs

6. $\frac{1}{20}$ min = secs

7. $\frac{3}{12}$ min = secs

8. $\frac{2}{3}$ min = secs

9. $\frac{1}{3}$ day = hours

10. $\frac{1}{6}$ day = hours

11. $\frac{5}{8}$ day = hours

12. $\frac{7}{12}$ day = hours

C

Round these to the nearest whole unit.

1. $5\frac{2}{3}$ kg

2. $246\frac{1}{5}$ g

3. $11\frac{3}{8}$ km

4. $7\frac{3}{4}$ m

5. $104\frac{2}{9}$ ml

6. $8\frac{9}{11}$ km

7. $72\frac{3}{5}$ litres

8. $2\frac{5}{6}$ g

9. $392\frac{9}{20}$ km

10. $45\frac{4}{7}$ litres

11. $647\frac{5}{12}$ kg

12. $6\frac{7}{9}$ m

85

Fractions and Measures

D

These are the ingredients needed to make 16 cakes.

160 g flour
48 g cocoa powder
120 g sugar
144 g butter
4 eggs

What would be the quantities for
8 cakes?
4 cakes?
2 cakes?

E

Find $\frac{1}{5}$ of each of these amounts.

1. 25 litres   3. £1.50   5. 90 m   7. 65 km   9. 55 minutes

2. 30 cm   4. 75 kg   6. £1.15   8. 40 g   10. 85p

F

Write the answers.
1. A piece of wood 60 cm long is cut into quarters. How long is each length?
2. A jug holds 624 ml of milk. A third of the milk is poured into a glass.
   How much milk is there in the glass?
3. There are 28 children in a class. Three-quarters of the children can swim.
   How many children can swim?
4. A cake needs to cook for two and a half hours. The timer can only be set in
   minutes. How many minutes will the cake need to cook?
5. The tank in a car holds 32 litres of petrol when full.
   How many litres of petrol will there be when the tank is a quarter full?

Summary for Unit 8

A

Write the answers.

1. $\frac{1}{2}$ of 64   3. $\frac{1}{3}$ of 36   5. $\frac{1}{4}$ of 60   7. $\frac{1}{10}$ of 80   9. $\frac{1}{7}$ of 49

2. $\frac{3}{4}$ of 32   4. $\frac{7}{10}$ of 90   6. $\frac{2}{3}$ of 96   8. $\frac{5}{8}$ of 72   10. $\frac{4}{9}$ of 54

B

Write the pairs of fractions that are equivalent.

$\frac{9}{45}$ $\frac{1}{2}$ $\frac{12}{16}$ $\frac{2}{3}$ $\frac{30}{36}$ $\frac{4}{8}$

$\frac{12}{18}$ $\frac{5}{9}$ $\frac{1}{5}$ $\frac{3}{4}$ $\frac{5}{6}$ $\frac{10}{18}$

C

Copy these, putting in < > or = to make each one true.

1. $\frac{2}{3}$ ◯ $\frac{3}{4}$ 3. $\frac{1}{5}$ ◯ $\frac{3}{8}$ 5. $\frac{3}{4}$ ◯ $\frac{5}{6}$ 7. $\frac{5}{6}$ ◯ $\frac{13}{18}$ 9. $\frac{1}{2}$ ◯ $\frac{6}{12}$

2. $\frac{18}{27}$ ◯ $\frac{2}{3}$ 4. $\frac{7}{8}$ ◯ $\frac{21}{24}$ 6. $\frac{4}{9}$ ◯ $\frac{18}{36}$ 8. $\frac{25}{40}$ ◯ $\frac{5}{7}$ 10. $\frac{4}{7}$ ◯ $\frac{2}{5}$

D

Write these as whole numbers or mixed numbers.

1. $\frac{10}{4}$ 3. $\frac{25}{5}$ 5. $\frac{47}{10}$ 7. $\frac{18}{2}$ 9. $\frac{32}{3}$ 11. $\frac{40}{5}$

2. $\frac{12}{7}$ 4. $\frac{27}{6}$ 6. $\frac{53}{9}$ 8. $\frac{32}{8}$ 10. $\frac{31}{4}$ 12. $\frac{49}{6}$

E

1. $\frac{1}{4}$ hour = ☐ minutes   4. $\frac{1}{2}$ m = ☐ cm   7. $3\frac{3}{4}$ l = ☐ ml

2. $\frac{5}{6}$ minutes = ☐ seconds   5. $\frac{4}{5}$ cm = ☐ mm   8. $6\frac{1}{8}$ kg = ☐ g

3. $\frac{1}{3}$ of a day = ☐ hours   6. $\frac{7}{8}$ km = ☐ m   9. $5\frac{9}{10}$ km = ☐ m

87

Knowledge needed

✓ understanding of fractions, particularly tenths
✓ use of a number line

Helpful facts

Decimal point

The decimal point separates whole numbers from parts of numbers:

whole number ⟷ . ⟷ part of number

7 . 4

and pounds from pennies

pound ⟷ . ⟷ pence

£8 . 32

> < = symbols

> means is larger than   0.4 > 0.14
< means is smaller than   2.3 < 2.51
= means is equal to $\frac{1}{4}$ = 0.25

Tenths and hundredths

The decimal point separates whole numbers from parts of numbers:

$\frac{1}{10}$ = 0.1 $\frac{3}{10}$ = 0.3 $\frac{5}{10}$ = 0.5

$\frac{2}{10}$ = 0.2 $\frac{4}{10}$ = 0.4

tens	units	$\frac{1}{10}$	$\frac{1}{100}$
1	7	2	
3	4	5	8
	8	0	6

The decimal point comes between whole numbers and tenths:

whole number   tenths
6 . 8

Hundredths is that place to the right of the tenths:

0 . 4 2 = $\frac{42}{100}$

4 tenths   2 hundredths

Writing fractions as decimals

Tenths and hundredths can be written as decimals:

$\frac{7}{10} = 0.7$ $\qquad$ $\frac{6}{100} = 0.06$

$\frac{35}{100} = 0.35$

Common fractions and decimals

$\frac{1}{2} = 0.50$ $\qquad$ $\frac{1}{10} = 0.1$

$\frac{1}{4} = 0.25$ $\qquad$ $\frac{3}{4} = 0.75$

$\frac{1}{3}$ makes a special sort of decimal – it recurs 0.333333…

Writing decimals as fractions

Decimals can be written as fractions:

$0.3 = \frac{3}{10}$ $\qquad$ $0.63 = \frac{63}{100}$

$0.5 = \frac{5}{10} = \frac{1}{2}$ $\qquad$ $0.75 = \frac{75}{100} = \frac{3}{4}$

Rounding to the nearest whole

If the decimal is less than $\frac{1}{2}$ or 0.5 round down otherwise, round up

$3.42 \approx 3.0$

$4.6 \approx 5.0$

$7.5 \approx 8.0$

Learning outcomes for UNIT 9

✓ knows tenths as fractions and decimals

✓ knows hundredths as fractions and decimals

✓ recognises the equivalence between fractions and decimals

✓ rounds decimals to the nearest whole unit

orders a set of decimal numbers

✓ adds and subtracts whole numbers and tenths

✓ solves problems with decimals in the context of money and measures

Tenths

A

What does the digit 4 represent in each of these?

1. 14.8   3. 42.6   5. 8.4   7. 4.3   9. 0.4   11. 420.3

2. 4.03   4. 406.2   6. 34.6   8. 2.4   10. 124.1   12. 49.6

What does the digit 9 represent in each of these?

13. 18.9   15. 29.1   17. 1.9   19. 94.7   21. 109.5   23. 24.9

14. 9.8   16. 946.2   18. 12.9   20. 36.9   22. 91.8   24. 69.3

B

Write how many tenths are in each of these.

1. 0.6   3. 0.1   5. 0.3   7. 3.5   9. 12.6   11. 17.8

2. 0.4   4. 0.8   6. 0.7   8. 1.9   10. 45.2   12. 60.9

C

Write these as decimals.

1. $4\frac{1}{10}$ 4. $1\frac{2}{10}$ 7. $18\frac{3}{10}$ 10. $76\frac{5}{10}$

2. $3\frac{5}{10}$ 5. $9\frac{7}{10}$ 8. $52\frac{8}{10}$ 11. $15\frac{7}{10}$

3. $8\frac{9}{10}$ 6. $4\frac{4}{10}$ 9. $20\frac{6}{10}$ 12. $48\frac{8}{10}$

Tenths

D

Rearrange each of these sets to make a number as near as possible to 6.

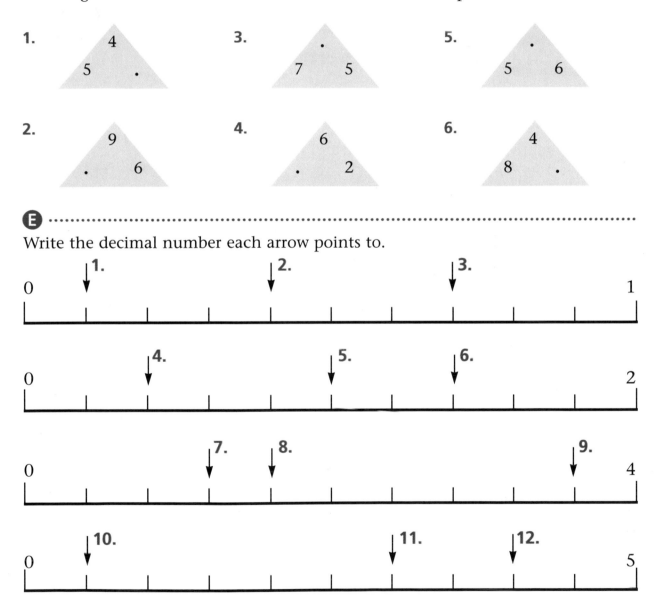

1.
4
5   •

3.
•
7   5

5.
•
5   6

2.
9
•   6

4.
6
•   2

6.
4
8   •

E

Write the decimal number each arrow points to.

9.2

Hundredths

A ....

What does the digit 8 represent in each of these?

1. 30.08   **2.** 41.8   **3.** 18.96   **4.** 72.48   **5.** 85.13   **6.** 59.87

What does the digit 3 represent in each of these?

7. 63.02   **8.** 40.38   **9.** 6.03   **10.** 28.31   **11.** 19.93   **12.** 30.07

B ....

Write how many hundredths are in each of these.

1. 0.68   **3.** 0.18   **5.** 0.01   **7.** 5.21   **9.** 7.06   **11.** 9.33

2. 0.05   **4.** 0.27   **6.** 0.92   **8.** 6.98   **10.** 3.14   **12.** 4.85

C ....

Write these as decimals.

1. $5\frac{17}{100}$ **3.** $7\frac{43}{100}$ **5.** $26\frac{26}{100}$ **7.** $9\frac{5}{100}$

2. $6\frac{80}{100}$ **4.** $14\frac{32}{100}$ **6.** $94\frac{18}{100}$ **8.** $36\frac{7}{100}$

D ....

Rearrange the order of these sets to make a number as near as possible to 5.

1.

1	.
5	6

3.

8	2
.	6

5.

1	6
.	4

2.

4	3
9	.

4.

.	7
4	5

6.

0	.
6	3

E ....

Write the decimal number each arrow points to.

0   **1.** ↓   **2.** ↓   **3.** ↓   0.1

Fractions and Decimals

A

Write the shaded part of each shape as a decimal and a fraction.

1. [bar shape with 10 segments, some shaded]

2. [bar shape with 10 segments, some shaded]

3. [grid shape with shaded squares]

4. [circle divided into 10 parts, some shaded]

5. [vertical grid with shaded squares]

6. [bar shape with 10 segments, some shaded]

7. [circle divided into 10 parts, some shaded]

8. [grid with shaded columns]

B

Write these as decimals.

1. $\frac{1}{5}$

2. $\frac{1}{2}$

3. $\frac{3}{10}$

4. $\frac{4}{5}$

5. $\frac{9}{10}$

6. $2\frac{1}{2}$

7. $8\frac{1}{10}$

8. $12\frac{3}{5}$

9. $47\frac{7}{10}$

10. $30\frac{2}{5}$

C

Write these as mixed numbers and fractions.

1. 0.4
2. 0.6
3. 0.2
4. 0.9
5. 0.5
6. 3.8
7. 5.1
8. 9.3
9. 1.7
10. 15.4

D

Write these as decimals.

1. $\frac{1}{100}$

2. $\frac{17}{100}$

3. $\frac{50}{100}$

4. $\frac{8}{100}$

5. $\frac{62}{100}$

6. $\frac{91}{100}$

7. $\frac{3}{100}$

8. $\frac{75}{100}$

9. $\frac{24}{100}$

10. $\frac{4}{100}$

E

Copy these and write > < or = to make each statement true.

1. 4.8 ☐ $4\frac{9}{10}$

2. $1\frac{3}{4}$ ☐ 1.75

3. 7.2 ☐ $7\frac{1}{4}$

4. $6\frac{32}{100}$ ☐ 6.4

5. 2.05 ☐ $2\frac{1}{2}$

6. 9.14 ☐ $9\frac{14}{100}$

9.4

Comparing and Ordering Decimals

A

Write each set of decimals in order.

1. 3.4   2.7   2.9   **3.** 4.0   3.9   5.3
     2.4   3.8   4.7   3.4

2. 1.5   5.2   2.1   **4.** 6.8   7.2   8.2
     2.5   1.2   6.2   8.6

B

Write the next three numbers in each list.

1. 0.66   0.67   0.68
2. 23.45   23.44   23.43
3. 17.05   17.06   17.07
4. 9.34   9.33   9.32
5. 4.95   4.96   4.97

C

Copy these and write < > or = to make each statement true.

1. 3.7 ☐ 3.07   **4.** 9.01 ☐ 8.98   **7.** 6.82 ☐ 6.28   **10.** 8.9 ☐ 8.90
2. 17.59 ☐ 17.61   **5.** 26.30 ☐ 26.3   **8.** 75.65 ☐ 74.56   **11.** 3.11 ☐ 3.01
3. 8.40 ☐ 8.4   **6.** 42.08 ☐ 42.1   **9.** 49.01 ☐ 49.1   **12.** 5.05 ☐ 5.50

D

Write each set of decimals in order of size, smallest first.

1. 4.75 4.09 4.7 4.2 4.91   **3.** 32.09 30.29 32.9 30.2 30.92
2. 3.18 3.8 1.38 0.83 1.8   **4.** 0.56 0.7 0.06 0.65 0.5

E

These are the finishing times in a 100 m race.

1. Which athlete came first?
2. Which athlete came third?
3. Write the times in order, starting with the winner.

Runner	Time (sec)	Runner	Time (sec)
1	11.61	5	11.62
2	10.04	6	10.9
3	10.19	7	11.09
4	10.96		

Rounding Decimals

A

Round each of these to the nearest whole number.

1. 6.4
2. 8.9
3. 17.4
4. 18.5
5. 10.8
6. 1.2
7. 49.6
8. 30.3
9. 25.5
10. 8.0

B

Round these to the nearest £.

1. £5.47
2. £3.40
3. £1.98
4. £6.57
5. £10.04
6. £9.60
7. £17.25
8. £98.81
9. £8.50
10. £60.06

C

These are the heights of trees in metres. Round each tree height to the nearest metre.

1. 2.5 m
2. 6.8 m
3. 4.15 m
4. 8.68 m
5. 7.02 m
6. 9.3 m
7. 4.28 m
8. 6.5 m

D

Round these to the nearest 10p.

1. £1.23
2. £4.84
3. £6.39
4. £2.16
5. £9.07
6. £0.19
7. £ 3.75
8. £8.11
9. £2.45
10. £7.98

E

These are weights in kilograms of parcels taken to a Post Office. Round each parcel to the nearest 100 grams.

1. 3.48 kg
2. 7.82 kg
3. 10.65 kg
4. 1.42 kg
5. 12.17 kg
6. 5.35 kg
7. 4.91 kg
8. 6.20 kg
9. 11.97 kg
10. 4.06 kg
11. 9.99 kg
12. 1.03 kg

Adding and Subtracting Tenths

A ....

Write the missing decimal number.

1. 3.8 + 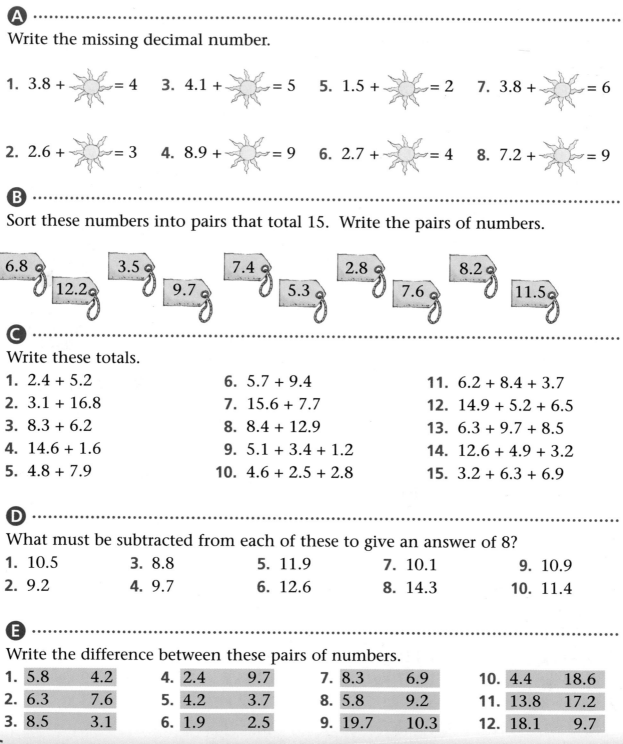 = 4   3. 4.1 + = 5   5. 1.5 + = 2   7. 3.8 + = 6

2. 2.6 + = 3   4. 8.9 + = 9   6. 2.7 + = 4   8. 7.2 + = 9

B ....

Sort these numbers into pairs that total 15. Write the pairs of numbers.

6.8 12.2   3.5 9.7   7.4 5.3   2.8 7.6   8.2 11.5

C ....

Write these totals.

1. 2.4 + 5.2	6. 5.7 + 9.4	11. 6.2 + 8.4 + 3.7
2. 3.1 + 16.8	7. 15.6 + 7.7	12. 14.9 + 5.2 + 6.5
3. 8.3 + 6.2	8. 8.4 + 12.9	13. 6.3 + 9.7 + 8.5
4. 14.6 + 1.6	9. 5.1 + 3.4 + 1.2	14. 12.6 + 4.9 + 3.2
5. 4.8 + 7.9	10. 4.6 + 2.5 + 2.8	15. 3.2 + 6.3 + 6.9

D ....

What must be subtracted from each of these to give an answer of 8?

1. 10.5	3. 8.8	5. 11.9	7. 10.1	9. 10.9
2. 9.2	4. 9.7	6. 12.6	8. 14.3	10. 11.4

E ....

Write the difference between these pairs of numbers.

1. 5.8	4.2	4. 2.4	9.7	7. 8.3	6.9	10. 4.4	18.6
2. 6.3	7.6	5. 4.2	3.7	8. 5.8	9.2	11. 13.8	17.2
3. 8.5	3.1	6. 1.9	2.5	9. 19.7	10.3	12. 18.1	9.7

Decimal Problems

A

Write the total cost for each of these shopping lists.

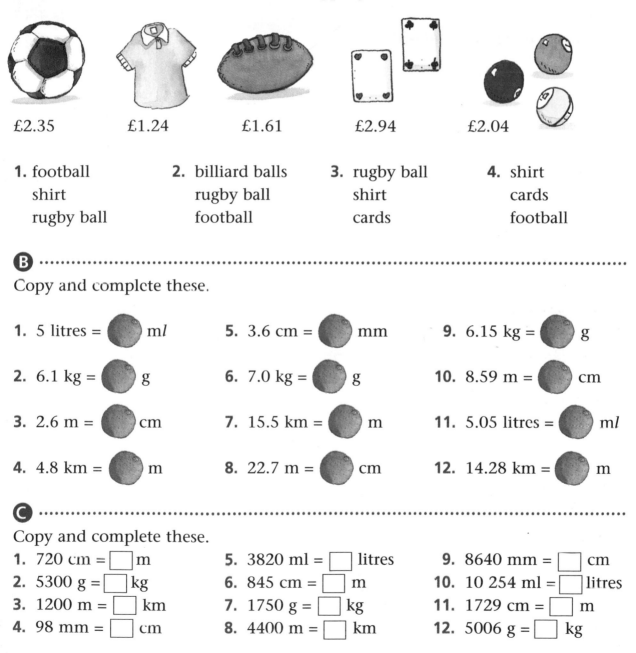

£2.35   £1.24   £1.61   £2.94   £2.04

1. football
   shirt
   rugby ball

2. billiard balls
   rugby ball
   football

3. rugby ball
   shirt
   cards

4. shirt
   cards
   football

B

Copy and complete these.

1. 5 litres = ⬤ ml

2. 6.1 kg = ⬤ g

3. 2.6 m = ⬤ cm

4. 4.8 km = ⬤ m

5. 3.6 cm = ⬤ mm

6. 7.0 kg = ⬤ g

7. 15.5 km = ⬤ m

8. 22.7 m = ⬤ cm

9. 6.15 kg = ⬤ g

10. 8.59 m = ⬤ cm

11. 5.05 litres = ⬤ ml

12. 14.28 km = ⬤ m

C

Copy and complete these.

1. 720 cm = ☐ m
2. 5300 g = ☐ kg
3. 1200 m = ☐ km
4. 98 mm = ☐ cm

5. 3820 ml = ☐ litres
6. 845 cm = ☐ m
7. 1750 g = ☐ kg
8. 4400 m = ☐ km

9. 8640 mm = ☐ cm
10. 10 254 ml = ☐ litres
11. 1729 cm = ☐ m
12. 5006 g = ☐ kg

Decimal Problems

D ....

Answer these.

1. Hannah is 1.34 metres tall. David is 9 centimetres taller.
   How tall is David in metres?
2. How much change would be given from £10 for two books
   costing £3.70 and £4.65?
3. One parcel weighs 3500 g and another weighs 1.5 kg.
   How much do they weigh together in kilograms?
4. A piece of wood is 450 cm long. 35 mm is cut off.
   How long is the piece of wood now?
5. A jug holds 2.8 litres. Two cartons of juice hold 1650 ml and 1200 ml.
   If the cartons of juice are poured into the jug, how much juice will be
   left over?
6. A runner runs 5.23km one day and 4790 m the next.
   How far in metres did she run altogether?
7. Mrs Greene buys a skirt for £17.35, a blouse for £14.50 and a jumper for
   £18.99. How much does she spend altogether?
8. Mr Khan buys a 3 metre length of ribbon. He uses 175 centimetres to
   wrap one parcel and 75 centimetres to wrap another parcel. How much
   ribbon is left?

Summary for Unit 9

Ⓐ ....

Write these as decimals.

1. $5\frac{6}{10}$ **2.** $57\frac{2}{10}$ **3.** $50\frac{60}{100}$ **4.** $49\frac{16}{100}$ **5.** $\frac{21}{100}$

Write these as improper fractions.

6. $2\frac{7}{10}$ **7.** $4\frac{1}{8}$ **8.** $5\frac{2}{3}$ **9.** $8\frac{5}{7}$ **10.** $10\frac{1}{2}$

Write these as mixed numbers.

11. $\frac{13}{4}$ **12.** $\frac{19}{6}$ **13.** $\frac{12}{8}$ **14.** $\frac{10}{2}$ **15.** $\frac{32}{5}$

Ⓑ ....

Write each set of decimals in order.

1. 6.01	6.3	0.68	6.1	6.38
2. 5.27	25.7	25.72	2.57	5.72
3. 14.9	13.09	14.02	13.92	14.22

Ⓒ ....

Round the following to the nearest 10p and to the nearest £.

| £2.31 | £7.49 | £10.04 | £4.99 | £21.50 |

Ⓓ ....

Write the answers.

1. 5.4 + 4.3   **3.** 2.8 + 3.6   **5.** 6.5 + 7.4   **7.** 9.7 + 5.5

2. 3.1 + 4.5 + 2.2   **4.** 6.3 + 5.4 + 9.1   **6.** 4.7 + 2.8 + 1.6   **8.** 7.9 + 4.2 + 8.8

Ⓔ ....

These are the distances each child travels to school:

Ryan – 1.02 km   Lizzie – 0.99 km   Megan – 1.95 km   Eliot – 1.12 km

1. Who lives furthest from the school?

2. Who lives nearest to the school?

3. Who lives the closest to 1 km away from the school?

4. In metres how much further does Eliot have to travel to school than Lizzie?

Knowledge needed
- ✔ understanding of fractions and decimals
- ✔ recognition of equivalent fractions

Helpful facts

Per cent sign: %

A number followed by the per cent sign (%) shows a fraction out of 100:

$$35\% = \frac{35}{100} \qquad 80\% = \frac{80}{100}$$

Common percentages

$$10\% = \frac{10}{100} = \frac{1}{10} \qquad 50\% = \frac{50}{100} = \frac{1}{2}$$

$$25\% = \frac{25}{100} = \frac{1}{4} \qquad 75\% = \frac{75}{100} = \frac{3}{4}$$

$$100\% = \frac{100}{100} = 1 \text{ whole}$$

Equivalent fractions

To change fractions to percentages, make the fraction out of 100:

$$\frac{7}{20} = \frac{35}{100} = 35\%$$

$$\frac{4}{5} = \frac{80}{100} = 80\%$$

To change percentages to fractions, make the fraction out of 100 and then simplify the fraction:

$$70\% = \frac{70}{100} = \frac{7}{10} \qquad 45\% = \frac{45}{100} = \frac{9}{20}$$

Decimals and percentages

Decimals can easily be changed to percentages by multiplying the decimal by 100:

$$0.35 = 35\% \qquad 0.7 = 70\%$$
$$0.08 = 8\% \qquad 0.97 = 97\%$$

Percentages can be changed to decimals by dividing the percentage by 100:

$$40\% = 0.4 \qquad 28\% = 0.28$$
$$10\% = 0.1 \qquad 5\% = 0.05$$

Percentages of amounts

To find 20% of £12, find 10% and double it:

10% of £12 = £1.20

20% of £12 = £2.40

To find 30% of £7, find 10% and multiply by 3:

10% of £7 = £0.70

30% of £7 = £2.10

To find 25% of 80p, divide by 4:

25% of 80p = 20p

To find 75% of 80p, divide by 4 and then multiply by 3:

75% of 80p = 20p x 3 = 60p

Learning outcomes for UNIT 10

✓ understands percentage as a fraction of 100
✓ expresses simple fractions as percentages
✓ expresses equivalent decimals as percentages
✓ finds simple percentages of whole number quantities

Percentages and Fractions

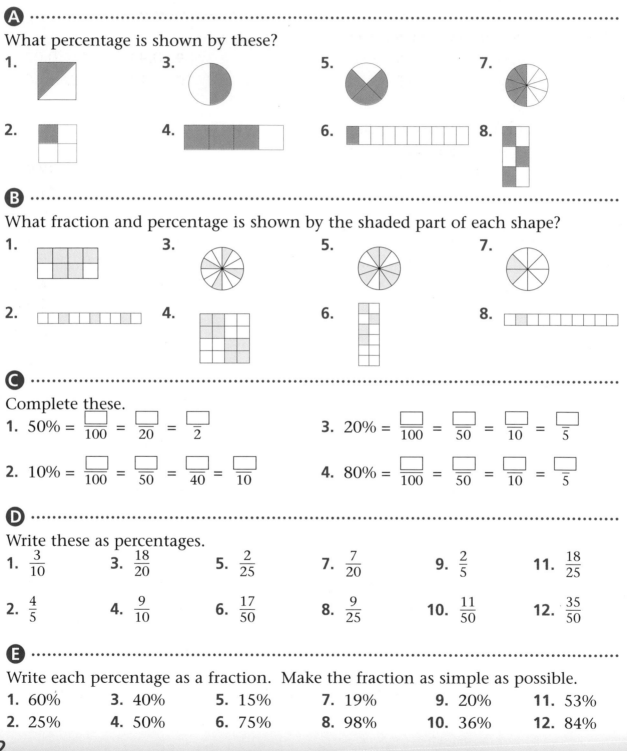

A

What percentage is shown by these?

B

What fraction and percentage is shown by the shaded part of each shape?

C

Complete these.

1. $50\% = \dfrac{\Box}{100} = \dfrac{\Box}{20} = \dfrac{\Box}{2}$

2. $10\% = \dfrac{\Box}{100} = \dfrac{\Box}{50} = \dfrac{\Box}{40} = \dfrac{\Box}{10}$

3. $20\% = \dfrac{\Box}{100} = \dfrac{\Box}{50} = \dfrac{\Box}{10} = \dfrac{\Box}{5}$

4. $80\% = \dfrac{\Box}{100} = \dfrac{\Box}{50} = \dfrac{\Box}{10} = \dfrac{\Box}{5}$

D

Write these as percentages.

1. $\dfrac{3}{10}$ 3. $\dfrac{18}{20}$ 5. $\dfrac{2}{25}$ 7. $\dfrac{7}{20}$ 9. $\dfrac{2}{5}$ 11. $\dfrac{18}{25}$

2. $\dfrac{4}{5}$ 4. $\dfrac{9}{10}$ 6. $\dfrac{17}{50}$ 8. $\dfrac{9}{25}$ 10. $\dfrac{11}{50}$ 12. $\dfrac{35}{50}$

E

Write each percentage as a fraction. Make the fraction as simple as possible.

1. 60%   3. 40%   5. 15%   7. 19%   9. 20%   11. 53%

2. 25%   4. 50%   6. 75%   8. 98%   10. 36%   12. 84%

Percentages and Decimals

A
Write these decimals as percentages.
1. 0.5   3. 0.6   5. 0.3   7. 0.25   9. 0.93   11. 0.07
2. 0.8   4. 0.1   6. 0.7   8. 0.75   10. 0.12   12. 0.45

B
Write these percentages as decimals.
1. 60%   3. 40%   5. 50%   7. 38%   9. 5%   11. 42%
2. 30%   4. 10%   6. 90%   8. 25%   10. 68%   12. 71%

C
Match each decimal with the percentage that it equals. Write the pairs.

0.6	0.9	0.06	9%	90%	45%
0.55	0.39	0.09	55%	6%	95%
0.95	0.3	0.45	60%	30%	39%

D
Copy these and write the missing digits.

1. $\dfrac{1}{\square} = 0.\square = 50\%$

2. $\dfrac{\square}{4} = 0.75 = 7\square\%$

3. $\dfrac{7}{10} = 0.\square = \square 0\%$

4. $\dfrac{4}{\square} = 0.8 = \square 0\%$

5. $\dfrac{1}{\square} = 0.2\square = \square 5\%$

6. $\dfrac{\square}{5} = 0.\square = 6\%$

E
Copy these and write > < or = to make each statement true.

1. 75% ____ 0.75   3. 50% ____ 0.5   5. 10% ____ 0.1

2. 25% ____ 0.4   4. 30% ____ 0.03   6. 63% ____ 0.36

Percentage Problems

A ....

Copy and complete this table of spelling test results.

Result	6	5	12	19	32	9	10	16
Maximum Total	10	10	20	25	50	20	10	20
Percentage	60%							

B ....

Find 10% of these amounts.

1. £8   **3.** £17   **5.** £36

2. £3   **4.** £16   **6.** £74

Find 20% of these amounts.

7. £6   **9.** £15   **11.** £41

8. £9   **10.** £27   **12.** £62

C ....

Calculate these amounts.

1. 20% of 100 metres   **3.** 50% of 150 m*l*   **5.** 60% of 72 km

2. 40% of 5 kg   **4.** 25% of 600 g   **6.** 15% of 75 m

D ....

Write which is the best buy in each set.

1. £12   or   50% off / £5 taken off

3. £80   or   reduced by £15 / reduced by 20%

2. £95   or   reduced by £15 / reduced by 40%

4. £60   or   25% off / £20 off

E ....

1. A bus has 50 passengers. 10 passengers have single tickets.
What percentage of the travellers have single tickets?

2. Kate gets £30 for her birthday. She saves 60% and spends the rest.
How much money will she save?

3. A cake weighs 400 g. 30% is dried fruit, 15% butter, 25% flour, 20% sugar
and 10% egg. How many grams of each ingredient was used?

Summary for Unit 10

A ....

Write these as percentages.   Write these as fractions.

$\frac{1}{4}$ $\frac{3}{10}$ $\frac{4}{5}$ $\frac{19}{50}$ $\frac{11}{20}$ 50%   90%   15%   52%   85%

B ....

What fraction and percentage is shown by the shaded part of each shape?

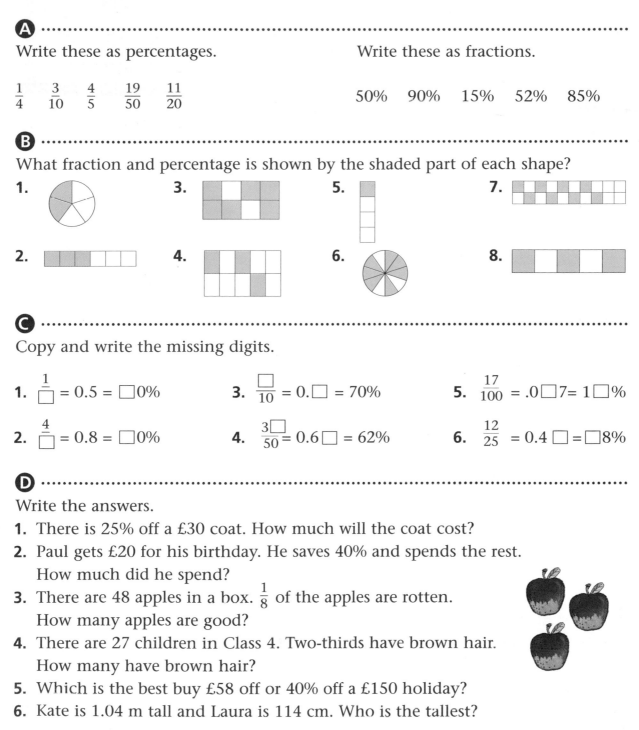

1.   **3.**   **5.**   **7.**

2.   **4.**   **6.**   **8.**

C ....

Copy and write the missing digits.

1. $\frac{1}{\Box} = 0.5 = \Box 0\%$ **3.** $\frac{\Box}{10} = 0.\Box = 70\%$ **5.** $\frac{17}{100} = .0\Box 7 = 1\Box\%$

2. $\frac{4}{\Box} = 0.8 = \Box 0\%$ **4.** $\frac{3\Box}{50} = 0.6\Box = 62\%$ **6.** $\frac{12}{25} = 0.4\Box = \Box 8\%$

D ....

Write the answers.

1. There is 25% off a £30 coat. How much will the coat cost?
2. Paul gets £20 for his birthday. He saves 40% and spends the rest.
   How much did he spend?
3. There are 48 apples in a box. $\frac{1}{8}$ of the apples are rotten.
   How many apples are good?
4. There are 27 children in Class 4. Two-thirds have brown hair.
   How many have brown hair?
5. Which is the best buy £58 off or 40% off a £150 holiday?
6. Kate is 1.04 m tall and Laura is 114 cm. Who is the tallest?

Knowledge needed
✓ telling the time
✓ the concept of the passing of time

Helpful facts

Reading time

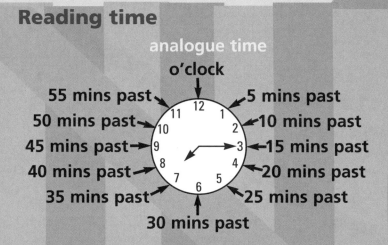

analogue time

o'clock

55 mins past
50 mins past
45 mins past
40 mins past
35 mins past
30 mins past

5 mins past
10 mins past
15 mins past
20 mins past
25 mins past

seven fifteen or 15 minutes past 7
• The small hand shows the hour
• The longer hand shows how many minutes past the hour

digital time

shows the hour

7:15

shows how many minutes past

seven fifteen or 15 minutes past 7

am and pm

| am means *ante meridiem* | 6.35 am | 6.35 in the morning |
| It is any time between 12.00 midnight and 12.00 noon. | 11.05 am | 11.05 in the morning |

| pm means *post meridiem* | 3.45 pm | 3.45 in the afternoon |
| It is any time between 12.00 noon and 12.00 midnight. | 9.20 pm | 9.20 in the evening |

24-hour time

Instead of using am and pm,
24-hour time goes from
00.00 to 24.00.
am times look the same, but
add 12 hours to pm times.

8.50 am $\longrightarrow$ 08.50 hrs
11.15 am $\longrightarrow$ 11.15 hrs

1.55 pm $\longrightarrow$ 13.55 hrs
11.20 pm $\longrightarrow$ 23.20 hrs

am   pm

| 12.00 | 1.00 | 2.00 | 3.00 | 4.00 | 5.00 | 6.00 | 7.00 | 8.00 | 9.00 | 10.00 | 11.00 | 12.00 | 1.00 | 2.00 | 3.00 | 4.00 | 5.00 | 6.00 | 7.00 | 8.00 | 9.00 | 10.00 | 11.00 | 12.00 |

| 00.00 | 01.00 | 02.00 | 03.00 | 04.00 | 05.00 | 06.00 | 07.00 | 08.00 | 09.00 | 10.00 | 11.00 | 12.00 | 13.00 | 14.00 | 15.00 | 16.00 | 17.00 | 18.00 | 19.00 | 20.00 | 21.00 | 22.00 | 23.00 | 24.00 |

24-hour time

Learning outcomes for UNIT 11
✓ uses am and pm when reading the time
✓ reads the time from a 24-hour clock
✓ reads timetables accurately

Reading the Time

A ....

Write the times shown on these clocks.

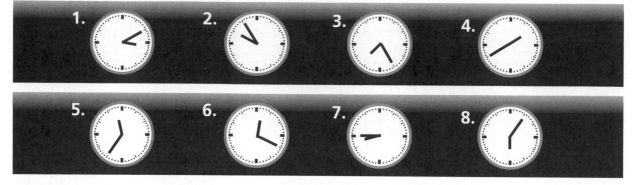

B ....

Write the times shown on these clocks.

C ....

Copy and complete this chart,
using digits and am or pm.

six thirty-five in the evening	6.35 pm
eight fifty in the morning	
twenty past eight in the morning	
quarter to ten in the evening	
ten to three in the afternoon	
quarter past eleven in the morning	

Write these
times 30
minutes later.

1. 8.26 am
2. 3.05 pm
3. 10.40 am
4. 7.55 am
5. 4.42 pm
6. 11.58 am

Write these
times 30
minutes earlier.

7. 9.43 am
8. 6.50 am
9. 3.00 pm
10. 10.10 am
11. 2.07 pm
12. 12.23 am

24-hour Clock

A

Write these times using 24-hour time.

1. 4.20 pm
2. 8.50 am
3. 1.35 pm
4. 6.15 am
5. 2.48 pm
6. 7.23 pm
7. 7.16 am
8. 11.33 am
9. 8.08 am
10. 3.05 pm
11. 11.00 pm
12. 10.02 am

B

Write which times are am and which are pm.

1. 09.00
2. 16.50
3. 10.10
4. 13.25
5. 06.30
6. 19.53
7. 20.38
8. 11.06
9. 08.02
10. 23.15
11. 16.00
12. 22.32
13. 07.17
14. 15.53
15. 20.20

C

Copy and write the missing times in this table.

three thirty-five in the afternoon	3.35 pm	15.35
seven fifteen in the evening		
twenty past eight in the morning		
	6.55 pm	
		22.05
nine forty-five in the evening		
	10.10 am	
		13.40

D

Write these times in order, earliest first.

| 08.32 | 2.24 pm | 13.50 | 02.30 | 4.40 pm |

| 9.48 am | 16.45 | 11.56 am | 20.19 | 8.09 am |

Time Problems

A ··

Copy and complete the times on this bus time table.

Bus 307

(Buses every 15 minutes between 7.40 am and 9.10 am)						
7.40 am	–	–	–	–	–	9.10 am
(Buses every 30 minutes between 9.05 am and 11.35 am)						
9.05 am	–	–	–	–	11.35 am	

B ··

Calculate the answers.

1. A candle is lit at 7.15 pm; by 9.35 pm it is completely burned down. How long did the candle burn?

2. A loaf of bread takes 45 minutes to bake. It goes in the oven at 10.24 am. When will it be taken out?

C ··

Mrs Day teaches piano. Each lesson lasts 20 minutes and she has one 10-minute break. Copy the table and write the start times for each lesson.

Start	3.45 pm			10 min			
Pupil	Laura	Ben	Imran	break	Beth	Ryan	Meerha

D ··

These posters show the times for different sports at a leisure centre.

Swimming lessons	Mon.–Fri.
4.15 pm – 4.45 pm	Beginners
4.45 pm – 5.25 pm	Silver
5.25 pm – 6.10 pm	Gold

Football practice
Saturday mornings
Start: 10.50 am
Finish: 12.15 pm

Gym class
Each class 45 mins
Mon., Weds. & Fri.
6.20 pm start

1. When does Gym class finish?
2. How long is the Football practice?
3. How much longer is the Gold swimming lesson than the Beginners lesson?
4. Football practice is now 35 minutes later. What is the new start time?

Summary for Unit 11

A

Write the times 30 minutes earlier than those shown on these clocks.

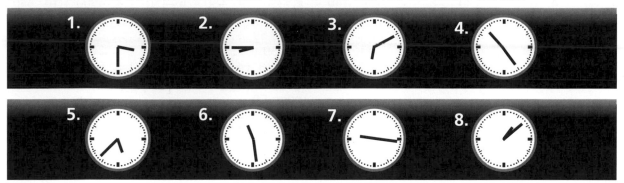

1. 2. 3. 4.

5. 6. 7. 8.

B

Write these times using 24-hour.

10.32 am   6.00 pm   8.02 am   7.14 pm

Write these times in the 12-hour clock using am and pm.

15.47   09.10   23.40   11.00

C

These times show how long it took to swim 400 m.

Luke	Isaac	Eve	Holly	Beth
8 min 35 sec	7 min 59 sec	8 min	9 min 2 sec	8 min 16 sec

1. Who was the quickest?
2. How much longer did the slowest swimmer take than the quickest?
3. Luke started at 4.30 pm. What time did he finish, to the nearest minute?
4. Beth also started at 4.30 pm. What time did she finish, to the nearest minute?
5. Eve started at 4.45 pm. Holly started when Eve finished. What was the time when Holly finished, to the nearest minute?

D

Write the pairs of times that have a difference of half an hour.

8.55 pm   Four fifteen in the afternoon   8.45 am   10.20

9.25 pm   9.50   Quarter past nine in the morning   16.45   **111**

Answers

112